**history
of the earth's
magnetic field**

**EARTH
AND
PLANETARY SCIENCE
SERIES**

Patrick M. Hurley,
Consulting Editor

history
of the earth's
magnetic field

DAVID W. STRANGWAY
Associate Professor of Physics
University of Toronto

McGraw-Hill Book Company
New York   *St. Louis*   *San Francisco*
Düsseldorf   *London*   *Mexico*
Panama   *Sydney*   *Toronto*

This book was set in Caledonia by The Maple Press Company, and printed on permanent paper and bound by Vail-Ballou Press, Inc.
The designer was Barbara Ellwood; the drawings were done by John Cordes, J. & R. Technical Services, Inc.
The editors were Bradford Bayne and James W. Bradley.
William P. Weiss supervised the production.

**history
of the earth's
magnetic field**

Library of Congress Catalog Card Number 76-118403

1 2 3 4 5 6 7 8 9 0 VBVB 7 9 8 7 6 5 4 3 2 1 0

preface

This book was written to fill the gap of an introductory book in the fields of paleomagnetism and rock magnetism. These are rapidly moving fields, and while it may be dangerous to write too dogmatically at this time, it was felt that the body of knowledge is now so great that a simplified outlook of these disciplines could be presented. No attempt has been made to cover every aspect of the subject nor to include reference to all the many individual contributions to the subject. Rather, the task was to present a series of chapters that would correspond to a series of lectures. Accordingly, detailed bibliographic references have not been made, and it is hoped that the many outstanding workers in the field will not feel "left out."

The material presented here grew out of a series of lectures originally given by the author at the University of Colorado as part of a course entitled "Rock Physics," and later it was presented at M.I.T. to a group of graduate students. Naturally, in writing this material, it was not possible to include all the detailed considerations presented in a lecture nor to include much of the discussion, which is the best part of any lecture.

The people who have assisted me indirectly in this work are many, and it is not possible to identify them all here or even to fully reconstruct the nature of the discussions with various people. I would, however, like to draw particular attention to Professor E. Larson of the University of Colorado and to Professor B. McMahon of Central State University, Ohio, with whom I have had many long discussions. They are not, however, to be blamed for inaccuracies or cases of unclear logic or thinking. Professor P. Hurley of M.I.T. encouraged me to write the book at this time. Without his prodding, I would never have completed it.

Finally, I owe a genuine debt of gratitude to my wife, Alice, who patiently put up with the "extra" hours required to write this book and who helped in assuring me that the material was both written in English and readable.

David W. Strangway

contents

APPENDIXES

introduction

In the study of the earth's history, there are very few physical quantities that have left any record. The study of seismology and of the earth's gravity field has revealed a great deal about the interior of the earth as it is at present. But these properties can be measured only for one point of time in the earth's history. It is possible to make inferences about what they may have been like in the past only by using hypothetical models. However, some properties of the earth are preserved, and have left direct records. Among these are temperature, length of day, and magnetic field. Extensive studies of temperatures in ancient times are being conducted using the thermally sensitive fractionation of oxygen isotopes in fossils. The temperatures of igneous rocks or those reached in metamorphism can be inferred by the particular assemblage of minerals present. Recent studies of the banding shown in typical corals and fossil shells have given an estimate of the number of days in a year at various times in the geologic past. Other evidence about paleoclimates includes the worldwide distribution of fossil types at various times, the indications of glaciation found in several of the continents, and the nature of sediments which form in different environments.

One property of the earth which does seem to be recoverable is its magnetic field in geologic history. This subject will be the topic of this book. The principle of paleomagnetism, or the history of the earth's magnetic field, is simple. At the time a rock is formed it often acquires a very stable, permanent magnetization. This magnetization, which is found in most rocks, usually points in the direction of magnetic north, and the strength of the magnetization is proportional to the strength of the magnetic field. If this magnetization, which is preserved in rocks, does not change through geologic time, it provides a good compass pointing to the ancient magnetic pole and gives us an estimate of the strength of the ancient magnetic field.

Studies of paleomagnetism are under way in many parts of the world, and it is dangerous to write too positively about the subject. However, the application of paleomagnetism to geologic problems has already progressed far, and it seems worth writing this monograph as a sort of progress report, indicating some of the fields of study wherein paleomagnetism is playing an important role.

This book is not meant to be a review of all aspects of the study of the magnetism of rocks. Books that cover these subjects in much greater detail have been published by Irving and by Nagata. These two books provide excellent summaries of our current understanding of paleomagnetism and rock magnetism, respectively. The book edited by Collinson et al., "Methods in Paleomagnetism," gives many of the details of instrumention and computational techniques commonly used in the study of magnetism in rocks.

In discussing the various aspects of the subject we will try to pursue a logical sequence. The first few chapters will be concerned with the physics of magnetism and with the magnetic minerals found in rocks that can carry permanent magnetism. The next chapters deal with the way in which rocks become magnetized and how we can test the magnetization. The rest of the book is concerned with a brief summary of knowledge about the present magnetic field and what we have learned about the ancient field. The final chapters deal with some of the exciting applications to such problems as continental drift and ocean-floor spreading.

1

the physics
of magnetism
and magnetic
minerals

Almost all rocks contain some magnetic minerals; therefore, with sensitive instruments it is possible to measure the magnetic properties of nearly every kind of rock. The minerals that carry the magnetism are usually iron- or manganese-rich and are limited in number so that we can discuss most of the minerals of interest quite briefly.

There are several basic types of magnetism that should be considered. These are diamagnetism, paramagnetism, ferromagnetism, and antiferromagnetism.

DIAMAGNETISM

The simplest picture of atomic structure involves a central nucleus with a positive charge on it. This charge is surrounded by negatively charged electrons traveling in orbit under the influence of the electrostatic force between the nucleus and the electron. One of the fundamental laws of electromagnetism states that any moving electrical charge generates a magnetic field. When the charged particle happens to be an electron and is traveling in an orbit, the magnetic field that is created is that of a simple *dipole*. That is, it has a field identical in appearance to the magnetic field surrounding a bar magnet with a north and south pole.

In a typical substance, these small orbital magnets are

TABLE 1-1 **Magnetic Susceptibility of Typical Minerals**

Diamagnetic:

Quartz	-0.5×10^{-6} emu/g	
Salt	-0.52	
Calcium carbonate	-0.38	
Gold	-0.14	
Galena	-0.34	
Silver	-0.18	
Sulfur	-0.48	
Ice	-0.70	
Zinc sulfide	-0.26	
Copper oxide (Cu_2O)	-0.14	Cuprite
Water	-0.72	

Paramagnetic:

Fayalite (Fe_2SiO_4)	100×10^{-6} emu/g	
Pyroxene ($FeSiO_3$)	73	
Biotite	53–78	
Garnets	31–159	
Amphiboles	13–75	
Cordierites	6–33	
Copper oxide (CuO)	3.25	
Manganese carbonate	100	Rhodochrosite
Manganese hydroxide [$Mn(OH)_2$]	152	
Manganese oxide (MnO_2)	40	Pyrolusite
Manganese oxide (Mn_3O_4)	54	Hausmannite
Manganese sulfide (MnS)	65	Alabandite
Nickel sulfide (NiS)	21	Millerite
Iron carbonate ($FeCO_3$)	98	Siderite
Titanium oxide ($FeTiO_3$)	0.87	Ilmenite
Titanium oxide (TiO_2)	0.07	Rutile

randomly oriented so that there is no overall resulting magnetism due to the orbital motion of the electrons. If, however, a substance is placed in a magnetic field, a force is exerted on each of the orbital electrons which tends to modify its orbit slightly (see Appendix 1 for a detailed analysis). The result is that the electrons slow down somewhat, and the magnetic properties of the material change slightly. Since the effect tends to oppose the applied field, the magnetization that is acquired in this way has a negative value and is referred to as *diamagnetism*. If we call the magnetism of the substance M and the applied magnetic field H, we find that M is proportional to H. The constant of proportionality K is known as the *susceptibility* and is given by $K = M/H$, where K may be measured on a unit mass, a unit volume, or a gram molecular weight. All substances have diamagnetism, but many materials have other superimposed effects that obscure this weak magnetism. Many common minerals, such as quartz, feldspar, and salt, are dominantly diamagnetic and have small, negative values of susceptibility, as shown in Table 1.

PARAMAGNETISM

In addition to the orbital motion of electrons, it is also known that electrons spin on their own axes. There is a small dipole associated with this motion, but the strength of the dipole is not changed by applying an external magnetic field. The result is that each individual electron behaves like a small permanent magnet or compass needle. They are usually oriented in random directions, but in the presence of a magnetic field these small electronic magnets tend to line up in the direction of the field, giving an increase in the magnetism (see Appendix 1 for a detailed analysis). This effect is referred to as *paramagnetism*. In the periodic table, the atomic number gives the number of electrons present in each atom of an element, and each element has a different atomic number. In order to keep total energy to a minimum, the electrons are usually arranged in their orbits in pairs in such a way that the spin magnetic moments tend to cancel each other. If a substance has an even number of electrons, the spin magnetism cancels itself, and only the orbital magnetism remains important. If, on the other hand, an atom has an odd number of electrons, the spin magnetic effects do not cancel, and the paramagentism dominates. Thus all atoms or molecules which have an uneven number of electrons show paramagnetism, whereas most of those with an even number are diamagnetic. Of more interest from our point of view is the transition series of elements. In atoms of these substances there are overlapping electron shells, and it is possible to have as many as five unpaired electrons in a single atom. This can give rise to a very large magnetic effect. It is these atoms which play the major role in the other magnetic properties which will be discussed.

It is usual in discussing the magnetic properties of substances to speak of a fundamental unit of magnetism known as a *Bohr magneton*. The Bohr magneton is the magnetic moment of a single spin per unit of applied field, and it is often written as μ_B. The numerical value of this is 0.927×10^{-20} erg/gauss. By knowing the Bohr magneton numbers of the molecules which make up a material, it is possible to calculate the bulk magnetic properties of this substance.

In natural minerals, only a few important ions actually carry significant paramagnetic properties, and most natural paramagnetism can be attributed to the presence of three ions. These common ions are Mn^{2+}, Fe^{3+}, and Fe^{2+}. The first two of these have a Bohr magneton number of about 5.59 μ_B and the third has a Bohr magneton of about 5.4 μ_B. On the average, that is, each of these atoms has about 5 or $5\frac{1}{2}$ unpaired electrons which are free to contribute to paramagnetism. A few typical values of paramagnetic susceptibility are given in Table 1-1 for some of the natural minerals of importance in rocks.

The measurement of the true diamagnetic or paramagnetic susceptibility of a pure mineral is difficult to make, since most natural minerals contain some magnetic impurities. Iron, in particular, commonly occurs in many materials in small quantities, and this can often override the susceptibility value for rock-forming minerals. An experimental relation between the total iron content and the paramagnetic susceptibility for a wide

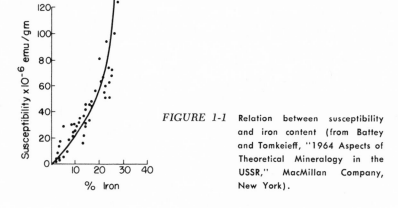

FIGURE 1-1 Relation between susceptibility and iron content (from Battey and Tomkeieff, "1964 Aspects of Theoretical Mineralogy in the USSR," MacMillan Company, New York).

range of minerals is shown in Fig. 1-1, illustrating the dependence of the paramagnetic susceptibility on iron ions.

The property of paramagnetism is a fundamental one in many rock-forming minerals, and it is primarily a function of the iron and manganese contents. Since, on one hand, a magnetic field tends to orient the spins and since thermal vibrations, on the other hand, tend to put the spins in random directions, it is clear that these are two opposing effects—the magnetic field trying to align the spins and thermal fluctuations trying to disorient them. The net result is that the paramagnetic susceptibility is a property that is strongly dependent on temperature. At high temperatures, where the disordering effects are large, the susceptibility is small, but at low temperatures the susceptibility is much higher. The relation between temperature and susceptibility is well known, and it is illustrated in Fig. 1-2 for a natural paramagnetic mineral (biotite). This curve has the shape which was recognized by Curie and is referred to as the Curie law (see Appendix 1). The relationship is such that the inverse of the susceptibility is directly proportional to the temperature. This property is one that is of considerable interest, as we shall see later, since sometimes materials which have a permanent magnetism can behave much like this, and it is necessary to take care to differentiate between them.

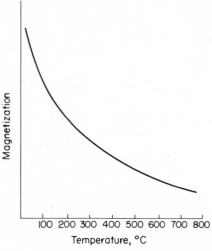

FIGURE 1-2   Relation between magnetization and temperature for a typical paramagnetic substance—biotite.

FERROMAGNETISM

When considering the history of the earth's magnetic field we are far more interested in those substances which carry a permanent magnetism, since it is this property which carries the information about the ancient magnetic field of the earth. Diamagnetism and paramagnetism are types of magnetism that exist only in the presence of an external magnetic field, and if the applied field is removed, the magnetism is lost. The basis of ferromagnetic properties, or those properties of a material that allow it to have a magnetization even in the absence of a field, i.e., a spontaneous magnetization, is the interaction between spins in nearby atoms in a solid material. So far we have ignored the possibility that one magnetic atom can act on another. These interactions are most important among atoms of the transition series of elements, where there are several unbalanced spins in each atom. As these atoms are brought together to form a crystal, there is a type of interaction commonly referred to as *exchange energy*. In most substances this exchange energy is reduced to a minimum when atoms are lined up in such a way that the spins in neighboring atoms are in opposite directions so that there is a cancellation of the magnetic effects of the individual spins. In a few substances, however, it is energetically desirable for these atoms to line up in such a way that the spins in neighboring atoms are parallel to each other rather than antiparallel, and their effects are additive. Such a material may have a strong magnetization, even in the absence of an external magnetic field.

There are various ways to describe this interaction energy, but the simplest description is to say that all the individual atomic spins behave as if there were a very strong magnetic field present inside the material which makes all spins line up. Although this internal field (sometimes called the *Weiss field*) is fictitious and merely a device for explaining the properties of ferromagnetic materials, the success and the simplicity of the model continue to make it a useful concept. The equivalent internal field is very large and is typically around 1 million oersteds, larger than any fields that have been created in the laboratory (Table 1-2). The result of this enormous equivalent field is that all the spins inside a substance are lined up and held rigidly in a fixed direction. It is not until other energies that tend to disrupt the spins become very large that such a substance loses its permanent or spontaneous magnetization. It is interesting to estimate the strength of this equivalent internal field by determining the Curie temperature. In ferromagnetic substances, it is found that heating above a certain temperature, referred to as the *Curie temperature*, causes the loss of all the spontaneous magnetization, and above this temperature the material behaves as an ordinary paramagnetic substance. At this critical temperature, the energy due to thermal vibrations overcomes the ordering energy due to the internal field. At the Curie temperature, the thermal-disordering energy then is just equal to the magnetic-ordering energy. From this, one can determine the equivalent internal field, as shown in Appendix 2. A typical curve of the spontaneous magnetization as a function of temperature for a ferromagnetic substance (magnetite) is given in Fig. 1-3.

TABLE 1-2   **Typical Magnetic Fields**

Earth's magnetic field:

equator	about 0.3 oe
poles	about 0.6 oe
Magnetic field at lunar surface	less than 10^{-4} oe
Magnetic field in a sunspot	1 to 40 gauss
Magnetic field of Venus at surface	less than 0.025 oe
Field of a typical laboratory magnet	10,000 oe
Field that can be achieved continuously	100,000 oe
Highest fields achieved in shock-wave experiments for fraction of a second	500,000 oe
Field at the nucleus determined by Mossbauer techniques:	
magnetite	450,000 oe
goethite	390,000 oe
hematite	510,000 oe
Equivalent Weiss internal field	(approx) 10,000,000 oe

This discussion does not cover the complete magnetic behavior of substances, since there are other energy relations that need to be considered. It requires a certain amount of energy, for example, just to maintain a permanent magnet with its free magnetic poles. This energy, often referred to as the *magnetostatic energy*, is dependent on the magnetic properties of a material and on the shape of a specimen. In general, nature prefers not to have free magnetic poles but would like to put north and south poles close together in order to cancel each other and so reduce the total energy. Thus, the exchange energy or internal field tends to line up all the spins, while the magnetostatic effect attempts to prevent them from lining up. The result is a balance of energy in which small zones, a few microns in size, are uniformly magnetized, but adjacent zones may have their magnetization pointing in some other direction. Large pieces of ferromagnetic material, therefore, may have only a weak overall spontaneous magnetization, although local small zones within the material have a large spontaneous magnetization. These zones are referred to as *magnetic domains*, and do-

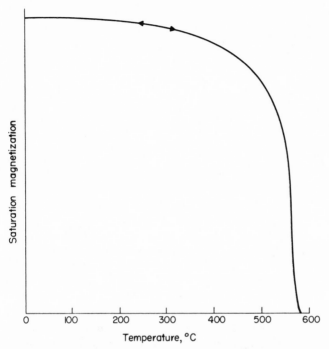

FIGURE 1-3 Saturation magnetization—temperature curve for a typical granitic rock containing ferromagnetic magnetite.

main walls separate the adjacent regions in which the spontaneous magnetization is in different directions. Some possible domain configurations are illustrated in Fig. 1-4.

The particular direction of the magnetization within each domain is determined by yet another factor. Within each crystal there is a group of preferred directions in which the magnetization tends to lie. This direction is known as the *easy direction of magnetization* and is determined by the crystal nature of the material. This dictates that the spins prefer to be oriented in certain directions, since every spin that is aligned in some direction other than an easy direction is not in a minimum magnetocrystalline energy state. However, in domain walls separating adjacent regions of uniform magnetization, some spins must

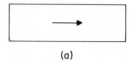

(a)

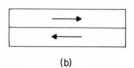

(b)

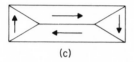

(c)

FIGURE 1-4 Idealized domain configurations:
a single domain.
b simple multidomain.
c multidomain with closures.

have directions of magnetization not in the preferred magneto-crystalline direction. These particular spins require extra energy to overcome the magnetocrystalline effect. The result is that it requires a definite amount of energy to form a domain wall. Such walls form only if they reduce the overall energy of the grain. The particular domain configuration present, then, is a result of reducing the total magnetostatic energy and wall energy to a minimum. The actual magnetic state of a material is thus determined by a variety of energies whose total must be reduced to a minimum. These are summarized in Table 1-3, and the ways of reducing each of them to a minimum are also indicated.

The basic ways of imparting a permanent magnetism to a substance can now be discussed. If we consider grains that are too small to have domain walls, we have an assemblage of single-domain particles. Such particles play a very important role in rock magnetism, and they will be discussed later in the chapter. Larger grains, large enough to have domain walls in them, behave in a characteristic way in the presence of magnetic fields. When such a substance is placed in a magnetic field, the domain walls can move fairly easy, allowing more of the

TABLE 1-3   **Magnetic Energies that Need to Be Minimized**

Type of energy	Cause	Method of reduction
Magnetocrystalline anisotropy	Preferred orientations in crystal	Align magnetization in preferred direction
Magnetostatic	Presence of free magnetic poles	Reduction in size of region of uniform magnetization and/ or elongation of magnetic zone
Wall energy	Ions oriented in direction other than preferred orientation	Make large regions of uniform magnetization and minimize wall area
Magnetostrictive	Stress creating anisotropy	Remove internal and external strains, e.g., annealing
Exchange energy	Interactions between wave functions of ions	Ions should be aligned either parallel or antiparallel, i.e., uniform magnetization

grain to be magnetized in the direction of the applied field. When the applied field is low, this is a reversible process and the domain walls spring back into place when the field is removed. The material behaves much like a paramagnetic material in weak fields. As the field is increased, however, the domain walls are forced over small imperfections and impurities in the grain and the walls cannot spring back to their original position when the field is removed. Only if the field is reversed can the magnetization be forced to come back to its original value. At this stage the process is no longer reversible, and a definite permanent magnetism is left in the substance after applying a magnetic field. When higher fields are applied, all the atomic spins line up in the direction of the applied field by overcoming both the magnetostatic and the magnetocrystalline energies. At

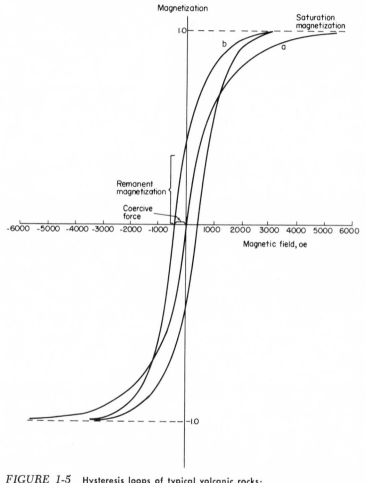

FIGURE 1-5   Hysteresis loops of typical volcanic rocks:
          a   rock with a considerable fraction of soft magnetization.
          b   rock with a considerable fraction of hard magnetization.

this point the substance has, in fact, spontaneous or saturation magnetization, as shown in Fig. 1-5. When the field is removed, the magnetization remaining is called the *remanent magnetization* or the *saturation remanence.*

In discussing rocks and minerals this magnetization has

often been referred to as the *isothermal remanent magnetism* (IRM), since no heating is involved in the magnetizing process. The reversed field required to reduce this magnetization to zero is the coercive force, which is often taken as a measure of the stability of the remanent magnetization. In studying the history of the earth's magnetic field, we are interested in the stability of magnetism, and we mainly wish to consider materials with a large coercive force.

In studying the remanent magnetism in rocks, we need to consider another way in which ferromagnetic substances can acquire a permanent magnetization. By the cooling of a ferromagnetic material from a point above its Curie temperature in the presence of a magnetic field, it acquires a weak, but sometimes very stable, magnetization referred to as *thermo-remanent magnetism* (TRM). Probably only a small percentage of any given ferromagnetic material actually contributes to TRM, and this is associated with those parts of a grain where the properties of that grain do not allow the domain walls to reduce the magnetization exactly to zero. TRM has a very important role to play in determining the history of the earth's magnetic field, and we will discuss more of its properties in detail.

FERRIMAGNETISM AND ANTIFERROMAGNETISM

In nature, the dominant minerals that carry a permanent magnetization are not simple ferromagnetic substances. Rather, the internal ordering of the atomic spins is quite complex. Both positive and negative exchange effects can exist in one material at the same time. The result is that some spins may be parallel to each other, and other spins may be antiparallel. If there is an equal number of parallel and antiparallel spins present, the material is called an *antiferromagnetic substance* (Fig. 1-6). Such a material behaves like a paramagnetic substance above a critical temperature at which thermal disordering disrupts the magnetic ordering. Below this temperature, often called the *Neel temperature*, the magnetic ions become locked in opposition, and the magnetization decreases with decreasing temperature, as shown in Fig. 1-7. A somewhat more general case is

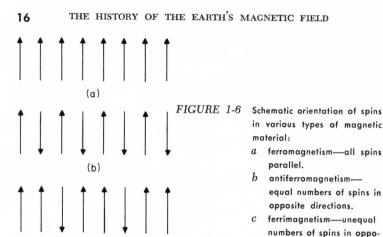

FIGURE 1-6 Schematic orientation of spins in various types of magnetic material:

a   ferromagnetism—all spins parallel.

b   antiferromagnetism— equal numbers of spins in opposite directions.

c   ferrimagnetism—unequal numbers of spins in opposite directions.

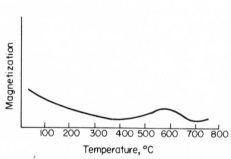

FIGURE 1-7 Susceptibility of antiferromagnetic hematite.

found when the number of ions in the parallel and antiparallel states are not equal so that the substance may be quite magnetic. Materials of this type are quite common in industrial applications and are referred to as *ferrimagnetic* or as *ferrites*. Minerals such as the very common magnetite and maghemite are ferrites. In a discussion of the remanent magnetism of rocks and minerals, ferrimagnetism and antiferromagnetism are most important, since all the common magnetic minerals are of these types.

In general, ferrites have bulk magnetic properties that are much like ferromagnetic properties, and it is only by careful studies that the differences can be distinguished. In general, antiferromagnetics, due to the spin cancellation, show bulk magnetic properties somewhat like paramagnetic substances. As we shall see, however, they can carry a weak remanent magnetism which can be important in paleomagnetism.

SMALL PARTICLES

multidomain–single-domain transition

Small particles have a special interest in the study of rock magnetism, since they occur very commonly and since their properties may be quite unlike those of large particles. A domain wall has a finite thickness usually estimated at about 100 to 200 lattice spacings. Any particles less than this in size must be single-domained, since they are not big enough to contain walls. The magnetic properties of a single-domain particle are quite different from those of a multidomain particle, since wall motion does not play a role in the magnetizing cycle. If we consider a simple material which has a single, preferred magnetocrystalline direction, the magnetization can be along only that axis. In the presence of a transverse magnetic field, the magnetic moment of the particle can turn and become parallel to the field, but on removing the field it returns to its original direction. Such a particle shows no hysteresis to a transverse field and has a magnetizing cycle, as shown in Fig. 1-8a.

If the magnetic field is directed along the preferred axis of this grain in opposition to the spontaneous magnetization, however, the situation is quite different. The magnetization can reverse itself if a sufficiently large field is applied to overcome the magnetocrystalline effects. When the field is then removed, it leaves a permanent magnetization in the new preferred direction. The field required to flip the magnetization is known as the *coercive force* and is shown in Fig. 1-8b. This type of behavior is of course highly idealized, but it represents the optimum condition to be achieved for maximum magnetic stability. If one then takes an assemblage of particles of this nature with random orientations, it is possible to derive an idealized hys-

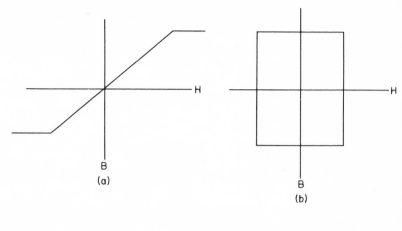

(a)

(b)

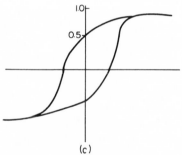

(c)

FIGURE 1-8 Hysteresis loops of single-domain grains [from Stoner and Wohlfarth, *Phil. Trans. Roy. Soc.* (London) **A-240:599** (1948)]:

a magnetization normal to the preferred axis.

b magnetization parallel to the preferred axis.

c hysteresis loop for a random assemblage of particles.

teresis loop for the overall group. The ideal curve is shown in
Fig. 1-8c. The optimum value of remanent magnetism/saturation
magnetization is given as 0.5 for a random distribution of single-
domain particles.

Thus small particles may behave as single-domain materials with a uniform magnetization. The anisotropy of the magnetism described above can arise in a variety of ways. As already
discussed, a preferred crystalline anisotropy can give these results. The field to reverse the magnetism is given as $2K_1/J_s$,

where K_1 is the coefficient of magnetocrystalline anisotropy and J_s is the saturation magnetization. Similarly, shape anistropy can give the same effect. It is easier to magnetize cylindrically shaped blocks along the long axis than across the material. This is a result of magnetostatic effects in which it is easier to have the magnetic poles far from each other. The field for reversing in this case can have a maximum value of $2\pi J_s$ for an infinite cylinder. A similar effect can be created by putting a particle under stress and giving it a magnetization in a preferred direction by the magnetostrictive effect. Thus a variety of causes can create anisotropy and hence hysteresis in single domain materials.

SUPERPARAMAGNETISM

At the limit of very small particles there is another factor which affects the magnetic properties. When particles are extremely small, they can undergo thermal vibrations which have energies of the same order of magnitude as the magnetic energy. The result is that very small particles of magnetic material do not have a stable magnetization, even though larger particles of the same material do. These effects have been ably described by Neel, who pointed out that the relation is such that the superparamagnetism is dependent upon V/T, where V is the volume and T the temperature. This behavior is very similar to that of paramagnetic materials, and hence the name *superparamagnetism*. Small increases in volume can change a particle from superparamagnetic to single domain, while small decreases in temperature lead to the same effect. Thus, a material which contains many small particles will have some particles which are superparamagnetic and some which are single domain. As the temperature is lowered, more particles become single domain and are referred to as *blocked*. This gives an effect that looks much like a distribution of Curie temperatures. The temperatures involved are less than the true Curie temperatures and often have a spread in values.

The importance of these small particles cannot be overemphasized, and a detailed discussion of their nature is given in Appendix 3. Superparamagnetism is generally considered to be the effect observed when a ferromagnetic or ferrimagnetic substance is broken up into very small grains, usually around 20 to 100 angstroms (Å). The substance loses its permanent magnetism when the thermal-disordering energy is equivalent to the magnetostatic energy. There is a second effect which is observed particularly well in antiferromagnetic materials. In this case the thermal energy becomes of the same order as the internal or exchange energy, and the antiferromagnetic material also behaves as a superparamagnetic one, in very small particle sizes. Typical estimates of 20 to 100 Å are given for the transition from antiferromagnetic to superparamagnetic. This same transition leads to other intriguing properties discussed in Chap. 2.

2

the magnetic properties of minerals

In this chapter we will discuss the magnetic properties of some of the important natural minerals that can carry permanent magnetization in rocks. It is important to understand these properties, since many rocks can have more than one magnetic phase which carries natural remanent magnetization (NRM).

There are several important minerals and several important series of minerals whose magnetic properties need to be considered. The most important and most thoroughly studied group of minerals is the iron-titanium oxides (Fig. 2-1), which has a wide range of magnetic properties. The most common mineral in this group is magnetite (Fe_3O_4), which is a ferrimagnetic substance. Table 2-1 shows the typical properties of some of the ferromagnetic and antiferrimagnetic minerals.

IRON–TITANIUM OXIDES: CUBIC

magnetite (Fe_3O_4)

Magnetite is an inverse spinel mineral that has 24 iron ions in one unit cell. Of these, eight are in one group (A group)

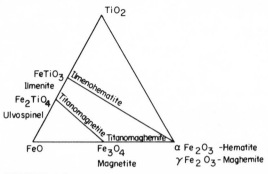

FIGURE 2-1 Diagram illustrating the composition of the major magnetic minerals.

and have their spins aligned in parallel directions. The other 16 (*B* group) are also parallel to each other due to positive exchange effects among themselves. This second, or *B*, group of iron ions, however, is aligned in opposition to the *A* group of ions due to negative exchange interactions. The result is that only 8 of the 24 iron ions present actually contribute to the overall properties of magnetite. Magnetite is therefore a typical ferrimagnetic substance, but it has overall properties much like those of typical ferromagnets. In Fig. 1-5, a typical hysteresis curve is shown. The saturation magnetization is large (about 90 emu/g). It has a well-established Curie temperature of 580°C, and when cooled from above 580°C in the presence of a magnetic field, it acquires a remanent magnetism often referred to as *thermoremanent magnetism* (TRM). Since the coercive force of bulk samples of magnetite is quite low, about 20 oe, it cannot generally be considered a magnetically stable material. As we shall see, however, when it is in very fine particle sizes, it can have high magnetic stability so that magnetite can be an important carrier of stable remanence. Magnetite has a characteristic brown color when viewed in reflected light.

One other interesting property of magnetite becomes apparent at low temperatures. At these temperatures, the coefficient of crystalline anisotropy (K_1) becomes zero. That is to say that at −143°C, the magnetocrystalline properties are no longer important. It is often found that the most stable remanent

TABLE 2-1   **Magnetic Properties of Minerals**

Ferrimagnetic	Curie temp or Neel temp	Saturation magnetization, emu/g
Magnetite (Fe_3O_4)	580°C	92
Maghemite (γ Fe_2O_3)	545 to 675°C	83.5
Ilmenite-hematite solid solution: $(x)FeTiO_3 - (1-x)Fe_2O_3$ $0.5 < x < 0.8$	50 to 300°C	21 (max)
Pyrrhotite $(FeS)_{1+z}$ $0<z<\frac{1}{7}$	320°C	19.5 (max at Fe_7S_8)
Jacobsite ($MnFe_2O_4$)	300°C	84
Cubanite ($CuFe_2S_3$)	Unknown due to polymorphic transition at 270°C	0.87
Magnesioferrite ($MgFe_2O_4$)	440°C	24.5
Trevorite ($NiFe_2O_4$)	585°C	51 (very rare)
Franklinite ($ZnFe_2O_4$)	60°C	
Chromite ($FeCr_2O_4$)	88°K	
Antiferromagnetic		
Hematite (α Fe_2O_3):		
antiferromagnetism	680°C (Neel temp)	
parasitic ferromagnetism	680°C (Curie temp)	0.5 (approx)
Ilmenite ($FeTiO_3$)	57°K	
Ulvospinel (Fe_2TiO_4)	120°K	
Pyrolusite (MnO_2)	84°K	
Goethite (α $FeOOH$)	120°C	
Akaganeite (β $FeOOH$)	77°K < Tn < 295°K	
Alabandite (MnS)	165°K	
Chalcopyrite ($CuFeS_2$) (high-temperature cubic phase is magnetic)	300°K	
Siderite ($FeCO_3$)	40°K	
Rhodochrosite ($MnCO_3$)	31.5°K	
Fayalite (Fe_2SiO_4)	126°K	
Troilite (FeS)	320°C	
Pyroxene ($FeSiO_3$)	40°K	

magnetization in typical rocks is unaffected by the process of cooling through this temperature and then allowing the sample to warm up in a field-free space. This is taken as an indication that magnetocrystalline properties are not important in determining the most stable part of the remanent magnetism. Since domain walls are controlled by magnetocrystalline energy, it is considered that in some rocks the very stable remanence is carried in single-domain grains. Magnetite is the most common of the magnetic minerals in nature, and we will see much more of its properties.

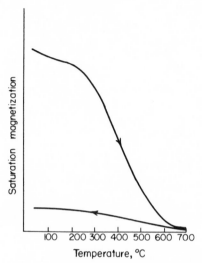

FIGURE 2-2   Saturation   magnetization
versus   temperature   curve
for   maghemite   showing
decrease of magnetization
on heating.

maghemite (γ Fe$_2$O$_3$)

The mineral maghemite is an oxidized version of magnetite and is also quite common. The overall properties are very similar to those of magnetite, its structure also being an inverse spinel structure but with a few missing iron ions. Much has been learned about this material, since it is used extensively in the manufacture of magnetic tapes. It is chemically unstable, and on heating to 300°C or more it converts to hematite (α Fe$_2$O$_3$), which has the same chemical composition but a quite different structure. A typical curve of saturation magnetization as a function of temperature showing the breakdown is given in Fig. 2-2. This should be compared with Fig. 1-3 for magnetite. Apparently it does not always convert to hematite on heating, possibly due to the presence of impurities which help to stabilize the maghemite structure. Because of the thermal instability of the mineral, its Curie point has never been measured directly.

Various reports indicate that the Curie point is somewhere in the range of 545 to 675°C.

Maghemite is present in many different rock types. In lava flows, it commonly forms at low temperatures of 200 or 300°C during the cooling process as the residual fluid reacts with the magnetite which has formed at higher temperatures and which then oxidizes. It can also form in other ways. In the sedimentary environment and in soils it forms by the low-temperature oxidation of small particles of magnetite in the presence of moisture. This maghemite is known to be the source of some of the remanent magnetism found in fine-grained sediments. It can also be formed in the laboratory by heating various minerals, such as pyrite to 400°C or lepidocrocite to 250°C. Maghemite can be recognized under the microscope in reflected light at high magnifications by its blue color.

magnetite-maghemite solid-solution series

The clear identification of magnetite and maghemite is difficult in many rocks, because the similar magnetic properties and structure make distinctive determination difficult and because apparently there can be intermediate compositions. Pure maghemite has a distinctive breakdown of magnetization on heating, as shown in Fig. 2-2. After heating to 500 or 600°C, pure maghemite appears to be completely destroyed, as shown by the difference between the heating and cooling curves.

ulvospinel (Fe_2TiO_4)

Ulvospinel is a mineral that is quite common but has often been overlooked when studying iron oxide minerals in rocks. It is now certain that it occurs in volcanic rocks, whose magnetic minerals are often rich in titanium. The structure of ulvospinel is similar to that of magnetite, except that one of the iron ions is replaced by titanium. The result is that the substance is no longer ferrimagnetic but behaves as an antiferromagnetic material, since there are equal numbers of iron ions on the two sublattices. It has a Neel temperature estimated at 120°K, well below room temperature. The important feature of ulvospinel in the study of rocks is that it forms a solid-solution

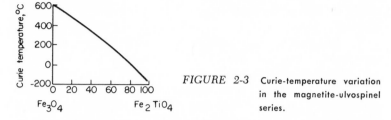

FIGURE 2-3 Curie-temperature variation in the magnetite-ulvospinel series.

series with magnetite so that intermediate members have properties between those of magnetite and ulvospinel. If titanium is present in magnetite, the Curie temperature is reduced, as shown in Fig. 2-3, and the saturation magnetization is also decreased. In many volcanics, iron oxides with Curie temperatures less than 580°C are present, and their exact titanium content can be studied by measuring the Curie temperature.

magnetite-unvospinel solid-solution series

Magnetite and ulvospinel form a complete solid-solution series, as just discussed, but in the process of cooling from a liquid state, there are often present residual liquids rich in oxygen and water. This residual liquid can react with minerals already formed with the general result that oxidation takes place. Ulvospinel forms at high temperatures, but during cooling it becomes unstable and oxidizes to form ilmenite and magnetite:

$$3Fe_2TiO_4 + \tfrac{1}{2}O_2 \rightarrow 3FeTiO_3 + Fe_3O_4$$

This ilmenite does not form a solid-solution series with magnetite, since it has a different structure, and exsolution into two phases takes place. The result is that small particles of magnetite and ilmenite are formed. Only the magnetite is magnetic at ordinary temperatures so that the material now consists of very fine grains of magnetic material separated by a nonmagnetic host of ilmenite. Many of these particles probably satisfy the criteria discussed in the previous chapter for single-domain behavior.

grain-size effects

It has long been known that one of the most effective ways of obtaining magnetic stability in magnetic materials is to have the material in extremely small particle sizes so that it tends to approach single-domain size. In the case of simple single domains, the coercive force is limited by one of the anisotropies of magnetization, since the formation of domain walls is not important. As discussed in Appendix 3, these anisotropies may be due to magnetocrystalline effects, due to shape effects, i.e., magnetostatic, or due to magnetostrictive effects. The limiting values of coercive force that can be achieved are given in the following table for magnetite:

		Limiting coercive force for magnetite
Shape $2\pi J_s$		2800 oe
for a cylinder		
Magnetocrystalline $\dfrac{2K_1}{J_s}$		600 oe
Magnetostrictive $\dfrac{3\lambda\sigma}{J_s}$		750 oe

where J_s is the magnetization (450 emu/cc), K_1 is the coefficient of magnetocrystalline anisotropy ($K_1 = -135 \times 10^3$ ergs/cc), λ is the average magnetostrictive coefficient (4×10^{-5}), and σ is the maximum internal stress ($\sim 3 \times 10^9$ dynes/cm^2).

It is clear that local internal stresses can give rise to a significant coercive force. Its importance can be shown in some cases by annealing and removing strains, thus reducing the coercive force. The magnetocrystalline effect is important also in the case of small single-domain particles which are equidimensional. The greatest coercive force and hence the greatest stability can be achieved quite clearly for long, thin, small particles in which the coercive force of an individual grain can theoretically reach 2800 oe. The stability of long thin particles is well known in the magnetic tape industry, in which attempts are made to obtain long thin rods of a magnetic oxide to put on the plastic tape base. Magnetite could be used, but small particles tend to be somewhat chemically unstable in air, and in general, maghemite, the oxidized version, is used by the tape industry. This has properties very similar to magnetite so that the above considerations are still valid. Great strides have been made by workers designing better tapes, and our understanding of shaped particles is much improved. Two factors need to be mentioned. For a single-domain particle about five times longer than wide, a maximum coercive force of 800 oe *has been* found. Apparently the theoretical limit of 2800 oe may be difficult to achieve, since the magnetization may not reverse itself coherently. When groups of particles are studied, the coercive force is invariably reduced due to the clustering effects. Many particles near each other behave in such a way that the effect of increasing length is reduced. The effect of increasing particle length and of removing near neighbors tends to increase the coercive force.

In nature we have one particular circumstance that probably simulates this closely. When an igneous rock forms, it is quite common to find well-developed exsolution textures of magnetic magnetite and intervening nonmagnetic ilmenite. The result is that very small equidimensional particles, rod-shaped particles, or flat platelike particles may be developed, depending on the nature of the exsolution. These rod-shaped particles might be quite uniform in shape and have length/diameter ratios of 10:1 or more. Moreover, they are well isolated from each other by intervening ilmenite so that the reduction of coercive force due to near neighbors is slight. As a result some individual particles may have coercive-force values which approach the maximum value of 2800 oe. This is indeed found to be the case, for many rocks have magetization which is stable in fields much greater than 1000 oe. Moreover, a direct correlation is found between rocks which show a great deal of the exsolution textures described and stability of the remanent magnetization. Thus both grain size and shape appear to be important in determining magnetic stability.

IRON–TITANIUM OXIDES: RHOMBOHEDRAL

In the iron-titanium oxide group of minerals there are two other important minerals which need to be considered. These are hematite and ilmenite, both of rhombohedral structure.

hematite (α Fe$_2$O$_3$)

Hematite has the same chemical composition as maghemite, but its structure is quite different. This substance is basically antiferromagnetic, but it can carry a superimposed weak ferromagnetism, often referred to as *parasitic ferromagnetism*. The magnetic properties of hematite still are not well understood, but its properties as presently known will be discussed. The antiferromagnetism has a Neel temperature reported as 680°C. At this temperature the iron ions are locked into antiparallel positions by the very strong internal field. Associated with this antiferromagnetism, some remanent magnetism can be acquired if cooling is in the presence of a magnetic field. The mechanism for this is not precisely clear, but it is probable that the TRM is due to the presence of a few spins which have no opposing spin so that there is a spin imbalance. This condition could arise in small grains in which there is an uneven total number of spins, or it could be due to the presence of local defects in the structure. Thus, as a very fine-grained hematite specimen is cooled from above the Neel temperature in the earth's magnetic field, it acquires a weak but very stable TRM. The material, moreover, does not show any hysteresis in fields up to 8000 oe, indicating that only a few ions in fact contribute to the observed remanence. In this respect, hematite is very similar to goethite, which will be discussed later.

In addition to the remanent magnetism associated with the antiferromagnetism, coarse-grained (greater than about 0.5μ) hematite can have distinct ferromagnetic properties, often referred to as *parasitic ferromagnetism*. The precise explanation for this is not clear, although several plausible mechanisms have been suggested. One of these is that the spins which are locked into opposite directions at 680°C do not remain locked in precisely opposite directions. At the same temperature (680°C) or slightly lower, they can acquire a small angle between them, giving rise to a weak magnetization at right angles to the spin direction, as illustrated in Fig. 2-4. This effect, referred to as *spin-canting*, could then be responsible for the ferromagnetic properties of hematite.

Hematite has other interesting properties. At −20°C (the Morin transition), it undergoes a structural transition in which the direction of the preferred spin orientation changes. At this temperature the weak ferromagnetism is also lost so

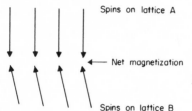

FIGURE 2-4 Effect of spin-canting in an antiferromagnetic substance.

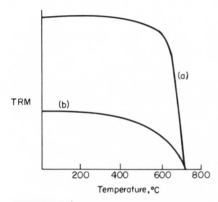

FIGURE 2-5 Thermoremanent magnetism acquired by hematite:
a with parasitic ferromagnetism.
b without parasitic ferromagnetism.

that the parasitic ferromagnetism is important only between −20 and 680°C. The TRM associated with the spin imbalance is, however, unchanged upon cooling through the Morin transition at −20°C. The weak ferromagnetism also disappears in small particles when the particles are less than about $\frac{1}{2}\mu$ in size, as predicted in the study of fine particles. This is the superparamagnetic limit for the weak ferromagnetism of hematite. The spin-imbalance remanence, however, remains in grains down to about 20Å. It is thus seen that the remanence of hematite can be explained as the superposition of two fundamental types of magnetism—one associated with the antiferromagnetism and due to a few spins with no mate and the other due to ferromagnetism

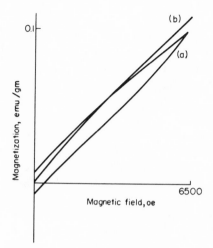

FIGURE 2-6   Partial hysteresis loops for
             hematite:
             a   with parasitic ferro-
                   magnetism.
             b   without parasitic ferro-
                   magnetism.

associated with spin canting or some similar bulk property phenomena (Fig. 2-5). The most interesting point about hematite in
rock magnetism is that it has a very high coercive force. The fine-
grained material with no ferromagnetism develops a TRM which
is extremely stable. The coarser-grained material with superimposed ferromagnetism has a definite hysteresis with a coercive
force of several thousand oersteds (see Fig. 2-6). Either type
of remanent magnetization shows extreme stability when compared with most other magnetic materials. It is for this reason
that hematite, although weakly magnetic, has considerable significance in paleomagnetism.

ilmenite ($FeTiO_3$)

The other common rhombohedral mineral that occurs
in nature is ilmenite, which is not magnetic at room temperature.
At $57°K$ ($-216°C$) it becomes antiferromagnetic. Ilmenite is
very common in igneous rocks but cannot play an important role

in determining the natural magnetization. It does, however, have one important function in the study of natural remanent magnetism and that is to break up grains of magnetite into smaller grains. In many volcanic rocks the content of titanium is high, and the iron-titanium oxide minerals formed are a mixture of magnetite and ulvospinel. As cooling proceeds, the ulvospinel becomes mineralogically unstable and tends to oxidize to form ilmenite and magnetite. Since ilmenite is rhombohedral and is structurally incompatible with the magnetite, an intimate intergrowth of magnetite and ilmenite forms. This material can readily be identified under the microscope in reflected light. A few typical microphotographs are shown in Fig. 2-7 to illustrate how ilmenite breaks up large grains of magnetite. The effect of this is to create great magnetic stability in the magnetite. The role of ilmenite is, therefore, of an accessory nature.

ilmenite-hematite solid-solution series

In the rhombohedral minerals, just as in the cubic minerals, there is a complete solid-solution series with interesting properties. So far we have not discussed the property of self-reversal. Now we need to consider this in detail. A few materials when cooled from above their Curie temperatures acquire a TRM which is opposite in direction to the applied field. Such materials are quite rare, but they are known to exist. The materials which acquire this reversed magnetization are generally ferrimagnetic, and they invariably have two magnetic sublattices, each with a different Curie temperature. The first set of ions acquires its magnetization parallel to the field, but due to the exchange coupling it causes the second group with a lower Curie temperature to be aligned in the opposite direction. If the second lattice, which is reversely magnetized, should be more magnetic at room temperature than the first lattice, the substance will have a net reversed magnetization. To date, the only reported natural material that shows this behavior is from a now famous rock in Japan known as the Haruna dacite. After much investigation it was found that the self-reversing properties of this rock could be attributed entirely to the presence of some material in the ilmenite-hematite solid-solution series. A portion of the composition range in this series behaves like ferrimagnetic

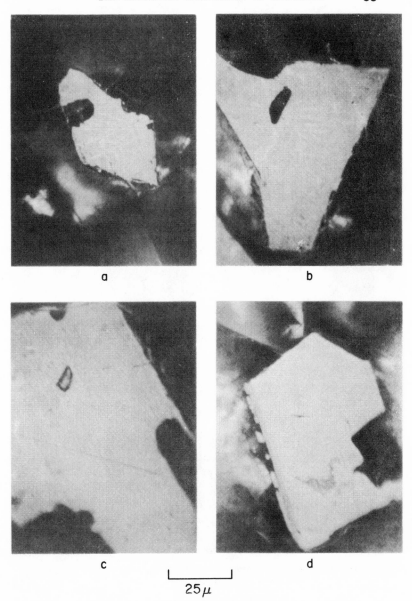

25μ

FIGURE 2-7 Photographs showing exsolution of ilmenite (light) and magnetite (dark) in typical oxidized volcanic rocks [from Strangway,
Larson, and Goldstein, *J. Geophys. Res.,* **73:3787** (1968)].

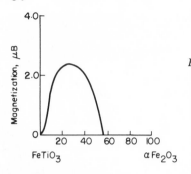

FIGURE 2-8 Composition of ilmenite-hematite solid-solution series showing range of ferromagnetic properties and self-reversing properties (from Nagata, Rock Magnetism, Maruzen Press, (1961).

FIGURE 2-9 Photomicrograph showing typical exsolution of hematite (light) and ilmenite (dark).

materials. The range of composition is between 50 and 80 percent ilmenite (see Fig. 2-8). This material is very highly magnetic and has the interesting property of self-reversal when cooled from above its Curie temperature.

Members of the ilmenite-hematite solid-solution series are quite common and are most often found in granitic rocks (see photomicrographs in Fig. 2-9). For this reason it is necessary to be quite careful about identifying reversals of the magnetic field, as we will discuss in detail in a later chapter.

IRON OXYHYDROXIDES

There are many other important minerals which occur in nature and a brief discussion of some of these will be given, since they are important in some cases. A group of minerals referred to as the hydrous iron oxides is quite common and is often referred to as limonites. There are four of these minerals known: goethite (α FeOOH), akaganeite (β FeOOH), lepido-crocite (γ FeOOH), and the fourth one (δ FeOOH) which has not yet been found in nature.

goethite (α FeOOH)

Goethite is commonly found in iron ore bodies and along with hematite and magnetite in weathered rocks. No clear-cut examples of natural remanence carried in goethite have yet been reported, but in the laboratory it has been shown to have magnetic remanence. It is known to be antiferromagnetic, with a Neel temperature at 120°C. When goethite is heated above 120°C, it acquires a weak but very stable TRM when cooled in a magnetic field. This is similar to the properties of hematite (Fig. 2-10). This TRM is almost certainly related to the presence of a few spins in the substance which have no mates. This may be a result of grain size or of imperfections present in the goethite as discussed for hematite. There does not, however, appear to be a superimposed weak ferromagnetism in the case of goethite, since no hysteresis phenomena have ever been reported. Evidently only a few isolated ions contribute to this weak remanence.

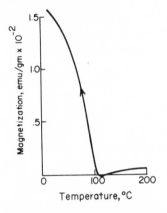

FIGURE 2-10 Acquisition of thermoremanent magnetism by antiferromagnetic goethite at its Neel temperature of 120°C (from Strangway, McMahon, and Honea, *Science*, 158:3802, 758 (1967). Copyright, 1967, American Association for the Advancement of Science).

On further heating, goethite usually dehydrates around 300 to 400°C and forms hematite.

akaganeite (β FeOOH)

This mineral is not common in nature and has a Neel temperature between 110 to 295°K, below room temperature. It is, therefore, not of significance in the study of natural remanence. On heating, it dehydrates to form hematite at 450°C.

lepidocrocite (γ FeOOH)

Lepidocrocite is a fairly rare mineral, but it is occasionally found in deposits of limonite as an accessory mineral with goethite. This material is neither antiferromagnetic nor ferrimagnetic at temperatures above 77°K, and so it can of itself carry no remanence. On heating it breaks down to form maghemite at 250 to 300°C. The maghemite so formed is unstable, and this in turn breaks down to hematite at about 400°C (Fig. 2-11).

Of the natural oxhydroxide minerals, only goethite appears to be an important, possible carrier of natural remanence.

PYRRHOTITE (FeS_{1+x})

Among the sulfide minerals only pyrrhotite has been investigated in detail. It is well known that pyrrhotite is a sulfide

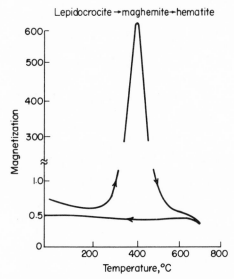

FIGURE 2-11   Saturation magnetization versus temperature for lepidocrocite (γ FeOOH) showing dehydration to maghemite followed by breakdown to hematite. (from Strangway, McMahon, and Bischoff, in "Hot Brines and Recent Heavy Metal Deposits in the Red Sea," Springer-Verlag New York, Inc., New York, 1969.

with a few missing iron ions in the lattice. These few vacancies play a very large role in determining the properties of pyrrhotite, since it is the unmatched spins associated with these "holes" that give rise to the magnetic properties. Natural pyrrhotite is commonly highly magnetic, behaving as a ferrimagnet with a Curie temperature at 320°C. The material carries a remanence, but in general it is quite soft magnetically, and it has not been extensively exploited in connection with the history of the magnetic field. It is also found that slight changes in the number of vacancies or in the ordering of the vacancies on the lattice vacancies cause large changes in the magnetic properties.

OTHERS

There has been very little investigation of the magnetic properties of the other sulfide minerals. It has been reported that pyrite (FeS_2) is paramagnetic at room temperature, whereas chalcopyrite ($CuFeS_2$) may be antiferromagnetic or even slightly ferrimagnetic in a high-temperature cubic phase. A tabulation of some of the ferrimagnetic and antiferromagnetic minerals is included in Table 2-1. In particular, the manganese oxide jacobsite ($MnFe_2O_4$) is ferrimagnetic at room temperature and carries a significant remanence, but it is quite rare.

Several minerals including cassiterite (tin oxide) and zircons have been reported as magnetic. It is likely that these properties are due to the presence of minor impurities of ferrimagnetic minerals.

3

magnetization in rocks

In the study of the ancient magnetic field of the earth we are particularly concerned with understanding the ways in which rocks can become magnetized by natural processes. We have already alluded to some of the possible processes in discussing minerals; we will now discuss the various processes in more detail as they relate to various kinds of rocks.

THERMOREMANENT MAGNETIZATION (TRM)

Many experiments have been done on igneous rocks to show that cooling from above the Curie temperature in a magnetic field causes the acquisition of a remanent magnetization referred to as *thermoremanent magnetization* (TRM). This TRM is accurately parallel to the applied field and for low-field strengths is directly proportional to it. All igneous rocks which cool from high temperatures acquire a TRM, and provided this is not modified subsequently, they will carry a memory of the field which caused the TRM. Although the details of the acquisition of TRM are not clear, it is known that materials which have large grains of homogeneous material tend to have a small and unstable TRM. On the other hand, if the grains are small, the TRM acquired tends to be large and more stable. It is well known that grain size is one of the important factors which

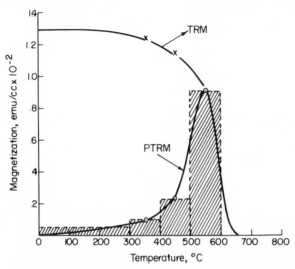

FIGURE 3-1   This figure shows the partial thermoremanence of the magnetization acquired in various temperature intervals. Sum of individual PTRM components add up to give the TRM curve.

controls the nature of the TRM acquired. Other factors such as the presence of imperfections or dislocations in the material may also be important.

Of considerable interest in this study is the law of *partial thermoremanence* (PTRM) discovered by Thellier and by Nagata. It is found that not all of the thermoremanence is fixed at the Curie temperature. If a substance is cooled through the Curie temperature and allowed to cool for a definite number of degrees in the presence of a field and the field is then removed for the remainder of the cooling, the substance will acquire a thermoremanent magnetism that is less than the total. It is found that if the sample is cooled in various temperature intervals in the presence of a field, the TRM acquired in each temperature interval is independent of that acquired in each of the other intervals. The total of all these PTRM values adds up to give the total TRM acquired by cooling from above the Curie temperature to room temperature in a magnetic field (Fig.

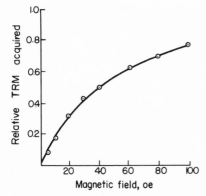

FIGURE 3-2 Dependence of thermoremanent magnetism (TRM) on magnetizing field for a typical volcanic sample (from Dunlop Thesis, University of Toronto, 1968).

3-1). This law of additivity is one of the interesting physical results of rock magnetism.

A simple physical theory based on single domains which accounts for many of the observed TRM properties of rocks was worked out by L. Neel. The theory is undoubtedly too simple to account for all the properties of rocks, but it does seem to work quite well for the remanent magnetism, as shown in Appendix 3. In any event, the single-domain theory predicts that the intensity of the magnetization should be dependent on the strength of the field, and for weak fields it should be directly proportional to it. This is in fact found to be the case in many igneous rocks (Fig. 3-2) so that one can measure both the direction and the strength of the ancient field in principle. This is the main subject material of paleomagnetism.

ISOTHERMAL REMANENT MAGNETIZATION (IRM)

Magnetic materials are also capable of acquiring a remanent magnetization without heating. This magnetization,

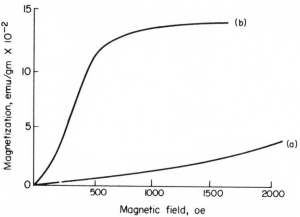

FIGURE 3-3 Isothermal remanent magnetism (IRM) acquired by:
a coarse-grained hematite.
b magnetite.

known to most people as the magnetization acquired by tapping an iron rod gently in the earth's magnetic field, is called *isothermal remanent magnetization* (IRM). Most materials are capable of acquiring an IRM which is dependent on the strength of the field applied to the specimen. This IRM can be readily demonstrated in the laboratory by applying larger and larger magnetic fields to a sample and measuring the remanence left after exposing it to the field. The value of remanence increases steadily, reaching a maximum referred to as the *saturation remanence*. The IRM acquired by magnetite and hematite is shown in Fig. 3-3 as a function of the field applied. In many natural materials, IRM is not a serious difficulty, since it is usually less than the TRM generated in the earth's field. For materials which are magnetically soft this is not always true, and tests to detect its presence are necessary. In one instance, moreover, nature applies a very large magnetic field which introduces a significant IRM. When lightning strikes the ground, it often causes the rocks to acquire a very large IRM. In field work it is especially important to avoid places that have been struck by lightning.

VISCOUS REMANENT MAGNETIZATION (VRM)

Unfortunately, as in many other geological problems, we must consider the problem of time. Exposures to magnetic fields for long periods of time can cause serious effects. This is the problem of *viscous remanent magnetization* (VRM), or time-dependent IRM. In the laboratory it can be shown that if a magnetic material is exposed to a magnetic field, it will slowly acquire a magnetization in the direction of that field. The process depends logarithmically on time at a fixed temperature, but at high temperatures it happens more rapidly (Fig. 3-4). The explanation is fairly straightforward. Thermal fluctuations which occur randomly tend to move domain walls slightly, and given sufficient time, there is a tendency for the walls to reorganize themselves to give a greater magnetization in the direction of the applied field. We know that this process can be important in rocks, since some rocks change their magnetization when stored in the laboratory even for a few months. Rocks whose *natural remanent magnetism* (NRM) are subject to large viscous effects are clearly unsuitable for paleomagnetism. It is possible to devise tests to detect these effects under laboratory conditions, but it is not possible to be sure that a VRM could not be acquired over a very long time or at a time in history when the sample was at a somewhat higher temperature. It is common to store the samples for several months to look for changes in magnetization, and it is also common to apply thermal and af cleaning (see later) to reduce the effect of VRM.

The only useful way to be certain about viscous effects in geologic time is to apply some of the classic field tests which will be discussed later. Typically, the field reverses itself every million years or so. If VRM effects were important in time scales of 1 million years, most rocks should have been remagnetized in the present field. For many rocks this is definitely not the case, since they are reversely magnetized and are not oriented in the present field. This field evidence shows that the time scales for remagnetization in many cases are greater than 1 million years. In some rocks, however, this is not true and they have been partially remagnetized in the present field. This gives

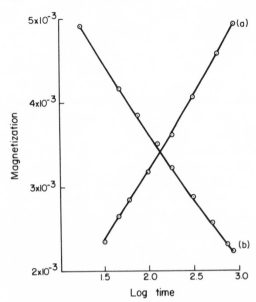

FIGURE 3-4 Viscous magnetization (VRM) in fine-grained maghemite

a growth in field of 16 oe.

b decay after removal of 16-oe field (from Dunlop Thesis, University of Toronto, 1968).

rise to the effect known as "smearing," in which the direction of magnetization lies somewhere between the original direction in the rock and the present direction. In this case the time scale for remagnetization due to VRM is less than 1 million years, and no meaningful paleomagnetism can be done using these rocks.

DEPOSITIONAL REMANENT MAGNETISM (DRM)

Sedimentary rocks have not cooled through the Curie temperature or the Neel temperature to give rocks a TRM, and yet most sediments do have some permanent magnetization which can be usefully detected and measured. The sediments that need to be considered fall into two major categories—those which have magnetic particles and which become aligned in the magnetic field during settling and those which have undergone post-depositional chemical changes in the iron minerals, introducing a subsequent magnetization. These latter processes may be particularly important in the case of red sediments in which many post-depositional chemical changes can be demonstrated. The question of chemical remanence and red sediments in particular will be discussed in the next section.

It has already been shown that small particles of magnetic material tend to have a high degree of stability. Therefore, sediments which are accumulating small pieces of magnetic material of 10μ or less in size might well acquire a stable remanence as the particles settle and are oriented by the earth's magnetic field. Fine-grained sediments tend to have a stable DRM. In fact, much of the early work in paleomagnetism was done on varved clays from North America and Sweden, and it was shown that these do in fact have quite a stable remanence. The evidence from these rocks most clearly demonstrates that DRM is important in many rocks. Mineralogical studies show that the main magnetic mineral is magnetite in very fine particle sizes of just a few microns.

Extensive laboratory tests have also been conducted in which materials have been resettled in the laboratory. These tests generally show that there is a tendency for the direction of magnetization acquired to be approximately the earth's field, but the inclination often tends to be shallow. This effect is referred to as the *inclination error*. It is probably due to the fact that small particles tend to have their magnetization aligned along the long axis of the particle, and these particles tend to settle into a horizontal position under the influence of gravity. Similar experiments have also been carried out in running water, in which case the inclination error becomes somewhat larger and more complicated. These laboratory experiments are generally carried out on materials which have a fairly limited distribution of grain sizes so that the magnetic particles behave mechanically in the same way as the nonmagnetic particles that make up the bulk of the sample.

Similar experiments involving a range of grain sizes have

also been done. In this case the inclination error is generally reduced, indicating that the orientation of some of the magnetic grains is controlled by the field with little mechanical action. It appears that as a moist sediment dries out and compacts to form rock, many of the magnetic particles settle in interstitial spaces between the larger grains. We have conducted many similar experiments using epoxies in which interstitial grains are refloated and allowed to settle in the presence of a magnetic field. The result in this case is that the direction of magnetization acquired is accurately parallel to the applied field. It appears, therefore, that depositional processes can lead to useful paleomagnetic data in some cases. The problem of inclination error is serious only if the particles of magnetic material have the same size distribution as the other grains. This might occur, for example, in a clean-washed beach sand where the particles are well sorted.

Of course, in very coarse-grained sediments where large pebbles which may contain magnetic materials are present, the deposition probably takes place in turbulent conditions and gives the sediment a random magnetization. Typical conglomerates in which magnetic material from the source rock is still present in pebbles generally do not acquire a magnetization that is oriented in the earth's field at the deposition site. The typical conglomerate thus has a rather weak and random magnetization, determined primarily by the hydraulic processes operating at the time of deposition. It is, therefore, possible to categorize DRM by the nature of the sediment involved and to make some reasonable estimates as to which types of sediments will be useful in paleomagnetic studies. The problem of acquisition of a secondary magnetization after the initial deposition needs to be considered in detail, since such processes may be very important in many sediments.

CHEMICAL REMANENT MAGNETISM (CRM)

Many people have discussed the possibility that remanent magnetism is acquired by a chemical transformation at a temperature less than the Curie temperature. It is clear that

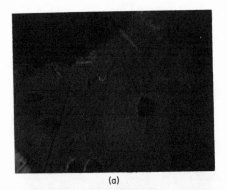

(a)

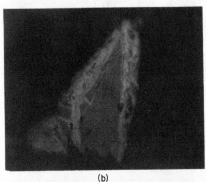

(b)

(c)

FIGURE 3-5

Photomicrographs showing changes in magnetic minerals due to weathering.

a fresh magnetite (dark) with very minor amount of hematite (light streaks) starting to form due to oxidation.

b magnetite (dark) with a considerable amount of hematite (light) formed by oxidation around edges and along cleavage planes.

c original magnetite grain almost completely oxidized to hematite. In the final stages of oxidation only minor almost undetectable amounts of magnetite remain.

such chemical changes happen in many cases in natural sediments. We have already discussed some of the magnetic minerals that occur in nature, and in many natural environments there is a tendency for minerals to oxidize. Thus, magnetite tends to alter to hematite in the weathering environment (Fig. 3-5). Since the magnetic changes that accompany this particular transition have not been studied in the laboratory, it is not certain whether the hematite acquires a remanent magnetization or if it does whether its direction is controlled by the original magnetite present or whether it is controlled by the ambient field at the time of the chemical transition.

The inverse process, that is, reduction of weakly magnetic hematite to highly magnetic magnetite, has been studied in the laboratory by the Japanese, and it is found that the magnetite does acquire a stable remanence that is controlled by the field acting at the time of the transition. This *chemical remanent magnetization* is referred to as CRM.

Similar experiments have recently been done in Russia, in which initially nonmagnetic minerals were subjected to a chemical transformation. In particular, lepidocrocite was heated to 375°C in a magnetic field and then allowed to cool in field-free space so that no TRM could be acquired during the cooling process. As discussed earlier, lepidocrocite forms maghemite on heating above 260°C so that a ferrimagnetic phase develops from an initially nonmagnetic phase. A distinct CRM is developed in the maghemite, controlled by the applied field, and this CRM is highly stable. In nature, other similar reactions are known to take place, even though lepidocrocite itself is not a common mineral. Other reactions that should be considered include the breakdown of some of the common rock-forming iron-bearing minerals in nature which are not ferrimagnetic. An extensive study of a series of sediments has been made in which iron silicates (in particular, hornblende) break down. Continental sediments contain hornblende which in the desert weathering environment alters rapidly to form clay minerals rich in hematite. This hematite is bright red and forms the pigment for many of the typical "red sediments" commonly found in the geological column. It has often been felt that the process of forming hematite could lead to the development of CRM as soon as the individual particles become larger than about 20 Å.

Once again, it is necessary to consider the time scale with which these changes are taking place. The earth's magnetic field reverses fairly often, and for much of the earth's history, changes in chemistry would have to take place in less than 1 million years in order for there to be a significant and coherent magnetization developed in this way. Compared to many of the chemical processes in rocks, this reversal time scale is very rapid. Even in rocks as old as 15 million years there are still extensive chemical changes taking place. If CRM is important in natural processes, it must take place in less than 1 million years, and it is, therefore, likely that it is not an important process. It can be demonstrated in the laboratory that heating typical red sediments to temperatures of 50 to 100°C and cooling in the earth's magnetic field causes them to acquire a small but very stable remanence. Thus, in sedimentary rocks it seems probable that extensive chemical changes which take place at room temperature over a long period of time do not cause the acquisition of a significant CRM. However, if the samples are heated after oxidation and reddening to temperatures of 100°C or so, the samples can acquire a TRM. Moreover, the heating process might also speed up the chemical changes and the development of hematite, leading to a combined CRM and TRM. Nagata has recently used the *thermochemical remanent magnetization* (TCRM) to describe this situation.

4

the present magnetic field of the earth and its recorded history

to discuss the history of the earth's magnetic field we must consider the nature of the present field, since it is only in recent times that we have any detailed knowledge about its variability in time and space. Unfortunately, detailed records of the field have been kept for only a few hundred years and then only at a few locations on the earth's surface. Now with navigation requirements for satellites and missiles, many continuing and detailed studies of the field are being conducted from ships, planes, and satellites. Since we are concerned here mainly with the history of the field, we shall discuss its origin and its variations.

ORIGIN OF THE FIELD

It was recognized early that the magnetic field of the earth tended to be fixed and to behave as if the earth itself were a magnet with its north pole pointing to the North Star. From this notion came the idea that much of the earth's interior was composed of magnetic material, probably iron owing to its great abundance in nature. The idea of a magnetic earth was quite appealing for a long time, and it provided an adequate explanation of the origin of the magnetic field. Detailed studies of the magnetic properties of typical materials reveal, however, that they are not magnetic above their Curie points and that at temperatures greater than a few hundred degrees (°C) no common material could possibly be magnetic. Since we know that the temperature increases in the earth at typical rates of 30°C/km or more, it is clear that at depths of 10 to 20 km any material likely to be present could not carry such a magnetization. Accordingly, one is left with the alternative of believing that the entire magnetic field originates in a thin shell a few kilometers thick or that some other mechanism is responsible. Since the magnetizations required for the thin shell are much larger than we observe in typical rocks, some other mechanism is believed to generate the earth's magnetic field.

Many other possibilities have been considered for the origin of the earth's field, but the only one that seems to stand up to continued investigations is the concept of a magnetohydrodynamic origin in the earth's core. In this theory, complex fluid motions in the liquid core give rise to a self-exciting dynamo which essentially keeps itself going. This self-perpetuation is accomplished by fluid motions in a good electrical conductor (the core) which distort the magnetic field lines. The simplest concept was put forth by Bullard and others, namely, that rotation of the earth and additional motion of the fluid within the liquid core are required. This second motion within the core could be due to a phenomenon such as convection, but it is important to realize that it cannot be a simple symmetrical motion about the spin axis.

The basic concept of the origin of the field is related to the fact that in fluids which are highly electrically conducting, lines of magnetic force tend to follow the fluid motion quite accurately. Thus an appropriate combination of fluid motions could cause the lines of magnetic force to be distorted and give us the field which we observe at the earth's surface. The condition which needs to be satisfied in order for the magnetic field lines to be tied to the fluid motions is given by the following dimensionless parameter, sometimes called a *magnetic Reynolds number,*

$$\frac{UL}{\lambda} \ll 1$$

where U is a velocity characteristic of the system, L is a length characteristic of the fluid motions, and λ is the electromagnetic diffusivity given by

$$\lambda = \frac{1}{\sigma\mu}$$

where σ is the electrical conductivity of the fluid, and μ is the magnetic permeability. None of these parameters is precisely known for the core, but typical values might be $\sigma = 3 \times 10^5$ mhos/m, $\mu = 4\pi \times 10^{-7}$ henry/m, and $L = 3 \times 10^6$ m. The fluid body then behaves as if the magnetic field lines follow the fluid motion, provided the velocity of the system is at least 10^{-6} m/sec or more. This is a very small velocity indeed, and there seems to be no doubt that such motions can readily exist in the fluid core. If the fluid motion of the spinning core has any shear motion to it (see Fig. 4-1), any small magnetic field present will tend to form closed field lines around the center of the earth. Such a configuration of field lines will form a toroidal field which has no surface manifestation. A simple shearing motion in the fluid core of the type just described and illustrated in Fig. 4-1 will not by itself give rise to the dipole field which we observe at the surface of the earth, and more complicated motions in the core are required to generate the observed field. Moreover, such a field is not self-sustaining and could be expected to die out in a characteristic time usually referred to as the *Cowling time* or the *free-decay time.*

This time is given as $L^2\sigma\mu$, where L is the radius of the fluid core. Substituting in the values quoted above, this gives a free-decay time of about 10^5 years. Since the record we are studying in this book suggests that the field has been present for most of geologic time, it is necessary to modify the situation so that the mechanism will become self-sustaining.

The details of this mechanism are not well known, but it is generally believed that additional motions in the fluid core can give us the required effect. The precise nature cannot be worked

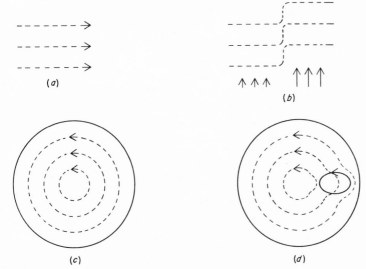

FIGURE 4-1   Toroidal field produced from an initial dipole field by differ-
ential rotation. This field is then modified by turbulent fluid
motion to produce a dipole field. (Dashed lines—field lines;
solid lines—fluid motion.)

a   magnetic field, undistorted.

b   magnetic field distorted by shear motion.

c   closed field lines due to rotational shear. These field lines
are then distorted by more complex fluid motion.

d   typical distortion that might be expected.

out, but it seems quite probable that any heat generated in the
fluid core or turbulence from other effects could cause the effect.
The processes that are generally considered are the following.

1   Radioactivity in the core could cause heating and hence
convective motion in the fluid. The required radioactivity
is only about 1 percent of that in rocks of the earth's
surface.

2   If the solid inner core is growing as the earth cools down,
it could release the latent heat of melting and cause
heating.

3   Pieces of the solid mantle could break off, and the movement of material through the core could cause stirring
of the fluid.

4   The earth is known to precess with a period of 26,000

years. It has been suggested that the ellipticity of the fluid core, which is different from that of the whole earth, would want to precess with a different period. In that case the core could get sloshed around as the more rigid part of the earth precessed and thus cause stirring.

5   A final possibility is that the earth, which is known to speed up and slow down slightly, could cause some stirring of the core, particularly if the core-mantle boundary is not smooth. In general, however, it is thought the changes in the length of the day are the result of fluid motions in the core rather than the other way around.

In any event it seems certain that some mechanism is stirring up the core and causing fluid motions other than those due to just the earth's rotation. These motions must combine in a particular pattern to distort the toroidal field which we have already discussed and give rise to the dipole, or poloidal, field which is observed on the earth's surface. This field is quite small compared to the toroidal field, but it is the only field measurable at the earth's surface. The presence of such a field is probably adequate to sustain the toroidal field so that although the toroidal field tends to die out in 10^5 years, the shear motions continue distorting the poloidal field and the field maintains itself. It is thus a closed circuit in which the toroidal field is maintained by shear rotational motions in the core and the poloidal field is the result of turbulent motions in the core which distort the toroidal field.

This, of course, sounds like perpetual motion, but it is not, since energy is required to maintain the system. Bullard suggested that the toroidal field might be as strong as 100 to 500 oe, whereas the dipole field at the earth's surface is only about 0.5 oe. At the core boundary this poloidal field is about 4 oe. The total magnetic energy in such a system is about 10^{28} to 10^{29} ergs, but the dissipation of magnetic energy is only at about the rate of 10^{16} to 10^{17} ergs/sec, based on an estimate of the free-decay time. This amount of energy could be fed into the system quite readily from a variety of sources, probably from the heat generated in the core or the rotation of the earth.

It appears, therefore, that it is possible for fluid motions

in the earth's core—both rotational and more turbulent motion—
to generate the earth's magnetic field in a self-sustaining way.
The detailed motions and mechanisms have never been worked
out, but the basic concept seems to be sound.

DESCRIPTION OF THE MAIN MAGNETIC FIELD

We have already mentioned that to a first approximation, the field is that of a simple magnet or dipole with a north
and south pole. Also as a rough approximation, the magnetic
north pole is nearly coincident with the rotation pole of the
earth. If we consider the magnetic elements that can be measured at a single location on the earth, it can readily be seen
that two horizontal measurements and one vertical measurement
specify the exact field at a single site (Fig. 4-2). Similarly, one
could measure various other combinations to specify the field.
One could, for example, measure the inclination of the field
or the dip below the horizon, the declination or the direction
of magnetic north, and the total field strength. This would also
fully specify the direction and strength of the field at the location. As early as 1600, Gilbert in his famous treatise "De Magnete"
had available sufficient observations of the magnetic dip over
the surface of the earth that he was able to recognize the essential dipolar nature of the earth (Fig. 4-3). Thus, simple observations of the direction of the field allow one to draw significant
conclusions about it.

By 1832, the powerful techniques of potential theory
were being developed, and Gauss applied it to a detailed analysis of the field. He used 84 stations scattered at 30° intervals
along seven lines of latitude. From this study he was able to
determine the first four coefficients of the spherical harmonics
of the earth's magnetic field. The use of spherical harmonic
analysis is very important in geomagnetism, since it can be used
to describe various complexities of the field. The field is well
described by the first-order coefficients which describe the dipolar nature of the field. Using the terms referred to as g_1^0,
g_1^1, h_1^1, the main dipole field can be described. The term g_1^0
measures the strength of the dipole along the rotation axis of
the earth. The terms g_1^1 and h_1^1 describe the strength of the

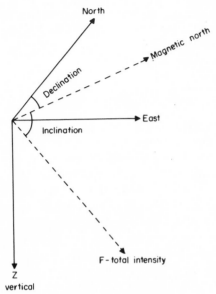

FIGURE 4-2   Typical magnetic elements which are measured at a site.

equatorial dipole, which is about 15 percent of the axial dipole. Gauss derived values of -0.3235, -0.0311, and $+0.0625$ for these three terms. These values can be used to show that the mean dipole-magnetic axis is presently $11.6°$ away from the present rotation axis. This corresponds to a field of about 0.6 oe at the poles and 0.3 oe at the equator. From this analysis it can also be shown that the position of the two dipolar axes are at $78°N$, $69°W$ and $78°S$, $111°E$. Since 1835, when Gauss made his analysis, many new estimates of the dipole coefficients have been made using data from a similar group of stations. Surprisingly, although the position of the main dipole is hardly changing, the strength of the field has decreased markedly from a magnetic moment of 8.55×10^{25} emu in 1835 to a moment of 8.06×10^{25} emu in 1955. This is a definite decrease which cannot be attributed to the use of improved instrumentation. If this rate should continue, the main dipole magnetic field will disappear completely in another 2000 years. We, of course, have

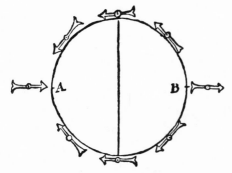

FIGURE 4-3 Sketch of a terella from Gilbert's "De Magnete" (1600) (from Dover Publications Inc., New York, 1958).

no way of knowing whether this trend will continue until the main dipole no longer exists or whether this is just a temporary phenomenon.

NONDIPOLE FIELD

In addition to the g_1^0, g_1^1, and h_1^1 terms in the spherical harmonic expansion, there are higher-order terms present in the harmonic expansions of the field (Table 4-1). These higher-order terms describe more local complexities in the magnetic field.

TABLE 4-1 Coefficients of the Harmonics of the Earth's Magnetic Field for the Field in 1835 and in 1955 (units of 10^{-4} oe)

	1835	1955
g_1^0	-3235	-3055
g_1^1	-311	-277
h_1^1	625	590
g_2^0	51	-152
g_2^1	292	303
h_2^1	12	-190
g_2^2	-2	158
h_2^2	157	24

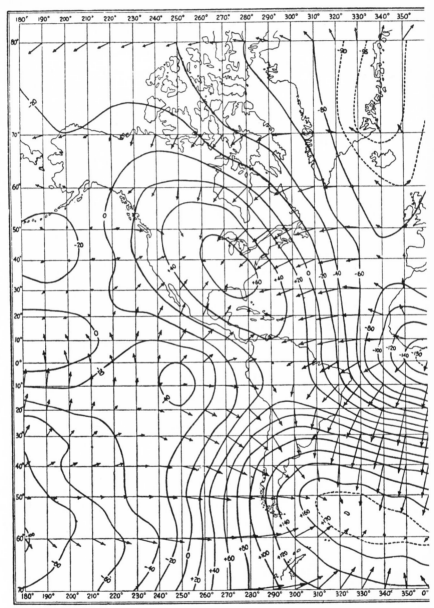

FIGURE 4-4 Nondipole field for 1945. Vertical field intensity with contour
Bullard, Freedman, Gellman, Nixon, *Phil. Trans. Roy. Soc.*

intervals at 0.02 gauss. Arrows give horizontal component [from
(London), A, 243:67–92 (1950)].

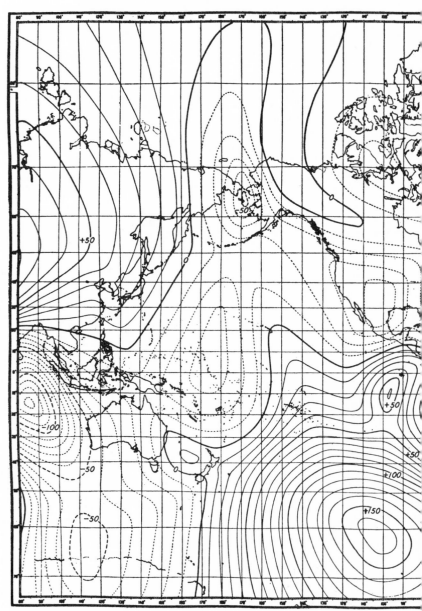

FIGURE 4-5   Geomagnetic secular change in gammas per year for period
Hendrix, Carnegie Institution Publications, p. 578, 1947.)

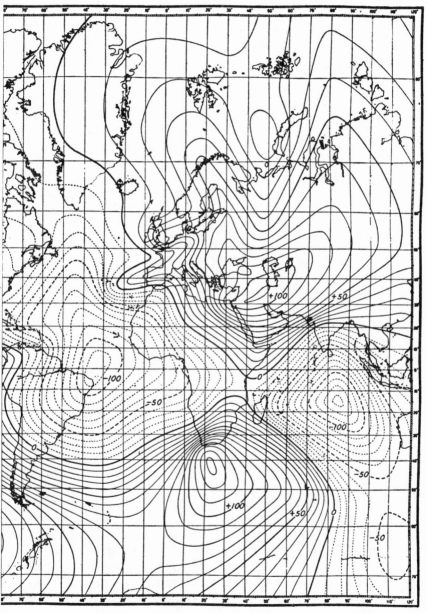

1940 to 1945. (From Vestine, Laporte, Cooper, Lange, and

Often referred to as the *nondipole terms*, they have an average value of about 5 percent of the main field at the earth's surface, although local variations as great as 0.18 oe exist. They form large centers located in various parts of the earth (Fig. 4-4). A great deal of interest centers around these features, since they appear to come from regions near the core-mantle boundary and may tell us something about the nature of that interface. It may well be that turbulent fluid motions take place at this boundary, creating local centers of fluid motion. These may distort the main toroidal field locally and give rise to these centers. We have no long-term information about the time changes of this nondipole field, but there do appear to have been characteristic changes in the last hundred years or so. In general, they appear to drift to the west in the characteristic motion referred to as *westward drift*. In the last hundred years, the main nondipole centers have shifted to the west by about 0.18°/yr on the average. This is not uniform for all centers; moreover, the features change their character somewhat as they move over the earth's surface, making it difficult to follow a single feature for a long time. The general appearance is similar to weather patterns. It should be pointed out that this variability in time is one of the important reasons for believing that the magnetic field is related to the core, since only in a fluid could changes this rapid take place.

SECULAR VARIATION

Another interesting set of maps referred to *as secular-variation maps* has also been prepared by various workers. It was recognized early that the magnetic field varied in time, and maps have been prepared showing the changes in the various magnetic elements. A typical map is shown in Fig. 4-5 for the differences to be expected in one year. This type of map bears a striking resemblance to the map of the nondipole field, and it shows typical changes up to 0.00150 oe/yr, with an average of 0.00050 oe/yr. This secular-variation pattern bears a distinct resemblance to the nondipole field, and it is generally felt that it reflects changes which are taking place in the nondipole field.

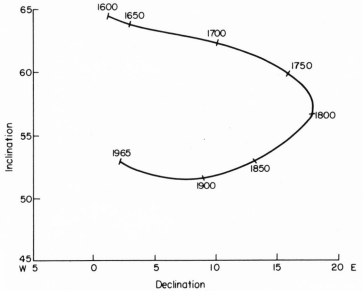

FIGURE 4-6   Secular variation recorded in Sicily.

Perhaps these more local terms are subject to more rapid changes than the main magnetic field.

It is interesting to note that in general the secular variation also appears to have a westward drift associated with it. Data from observation do not permit us to state with assurance that this characteristic drift to the west is a permanent feature of the field. As we shall see in Chap. 7, on archaeomagnetism, there is some evidence that the field can drift to the east as well as to the west. A plot of data from an observatory in Sicily (taken from Chevallier) is given in Fig. 4-6, showing how the local declination and inclination have varied since 1600. The most interesting feature of this type of plot is to note the clockwise sense of rotation of the secular-variation plot. This is to be expected in all cases in which the centers of secular variation are drifting to the west. In Fig. 4-7, data taken from a compilation by Yukutake show how specific features can be traced in time. In this case a peak in declination can be followed across Canada from St. John's, Newfoundland, in the east to Prince

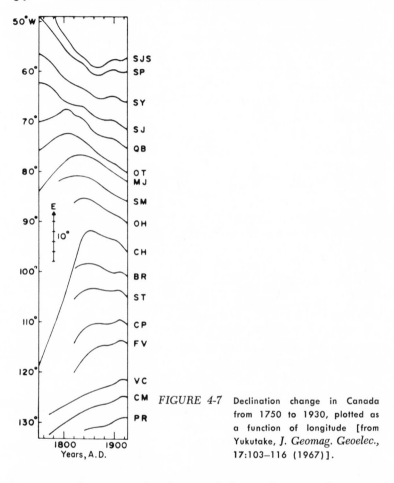

FIGURE 4-7   Declination change in Canada from 1750 to 1930, plotted as a function of longitude [from Yukutake, *J. Geomag. Geoelec.,* 17:103–116 (1967)].

Rupert in the west. This feature drifts at the rate of 0.4°/yr. It is interesting to note that the variations in declination appear typically to be over a range of 40° and the range in inclination over about 20°.

In determining the mean value of the direction of the field, these variations are clearly present, and they definitely need to be averaged out by taking time averages. It is presumed, in general, that an average taken over a few thousand years at a single location will yield the mean dipole position.

It is also of some interest to consider the possibility that some of the centers of secular variation may be longer lived than a few hundred or thousand years. It has been suggested by Hide, for example, that such features may be locked to irregularities in the core-mantle boundary. Unfortunately, again, observations made over limited time spans do not give us the full answer. It is interesting in this connection to note that the Pacific Ocean appears at present to be an area of low secular variation. Data from Hawaiian lava flows indicate that this may have been the case for many thousands of years. If this should indeed eventually prove correct, it will be necessary to account for the lack of secular variations in the area or to look for some difference in the mantle that screens out the effect. At this time we cannot completely exclude the possibility that secular variations will not average out, even in periods of several thousand years.

IMPORTANT POINTS

The important information about the magnetic field which we can derive from observatory data and which is helpful in interpreting the longer history of the earth is the following:

1 It is essentially dipolar.
2 The rotation axis and the dipole axis are roughly coincident.
3 The strength of the main dipole field has decreased significantly in the last 130 years.
4 There are important secular changes in the direction of the magnetic field in a few hundred years. These are related to large nondipole terms, and it is found that the compass deviates from magnetic north by varying amounts, up to 20° east or west.
5 At the present time, most of the time-varying features of the earth's field are drifting westward at the rate of 0.1 to 0.6°/yr. At this rate the average magnetic field could be measured at a single location by averaging measurements over a time-span of a few thousand years.

5

data analysis and tests of stability of magnetization

We have seen in previous chapters that there are many ways in which rocks can acquire remanent magnetization. In attempting to determine the history of the earth's magnetic field, it is essential to insure that the remanence measured is that acquired at the time that the rock formed. This is very difficult to do with certainty, since there can be changes or modifications that take place after the formation of the rock that we are not able to detect in laboratory tests. In particular, viscous and chemical effects can contribute important remanent magnetizations after formation of the rock. If these effects are acquired long after the formation of the rock, they have little use in paleomagnetism. Accordingly, many tests are used in paleomagnetism in an attempt to detect such effects. The tests fall into two classes. The first class tests the nature of the natural remanent magnetism that presently exists in the rocks. It is, for example, often possible to remove by various laboratory procedures less stable components of magnetization which may be due to viscous effects. This at least reduces the possibility that the components of secondary magnetizations, which tend to be less stable than the primary magnetization, play a role in determining the directions. These tests are extremely important, but they do not test for the possibility that a magnetically stable secondary magnetization has been acquired. This possibility can be tested in a few specific cases by applying the second class of tests referred to as *field tests*. The encouraging results of these tests lead us to believe that many rocks do have remanent magnetizations which are stable for geologic lengths of time. It is difficult to overemphasize the need for extensive testing of stability and the need to beware of secondary magnetizations. In much of the early paleomagnetic work, many of the techniques now used were not available to investigators. Accordingly, it is necessary to regard some of the early data with reservations, since studies of stability have not always been reported.

DATA COLLECTION

The problem of effectively sampling the ancient field is not a simple one. In attempting to determine a pole position, the usual method is to collect oriented samples through a sequence of rocks in an attempt to average out the secular variation discussed in Chap. 4. Simple firm rules have not been established to insure that this averaging is done. In studying volcanic rocks, one would certainly need to sample several flows. In a sedimentary stratigraphic sequence, it would be desirable to collect samples through a sequence which represents several thousand years. Since the processes of collection and measurement involve internal experimental errors of several degrees, the normal procedure used by most paleomagnetic workers is to take several specimens from each hand sample or core collected on which one set of orientation marks has been placed. Usually, then, six or more samples representing each condition to be tested are collected. Thus, in a single stratigraphic sequence or unit, one would collect at least six samples spread out in such a way that they represent a significant length of time. Although the approach to each individual problem varies, an attempt is normally made to average out the random errors from collection and measurement and from the possible effects of secular variation.

After making a collection of oriented samples, the next step is to measure the remanent magnetization and its direction in the sample. This is generally done on a simple magnetometer, usually an astatic magnetometer or a spinner magnetometer. In the first case, simple balanced magnets on a torsion fiber are used for the measurement. The deflection of the magnet system when a sample is brought near one of the magnets gives the magnetization. In the second case, the sample is spun opposite a pick-up coil. The magnetic moment of the sample generates a voltage in the coil which can be detected and measured. The basic procedure is to measure the direction of magnetization in the sample and, hence, to determine both the declination and the inclination of the magnetization at the sampling locality. With several specimens and samples collected, it is possible to determine the average direction of magnetization of the geologic unit under study. The normal analysis that is used is described in the next section.

DATA ANALYSIS

In analyzing results, it is normally assumed that the vectors measured in the samples are randomly distributed around a mean. With this basic assumption in mind, it is necessary to conduct statistical analyses of the directions at two levels. The mean direction of the specimens from a single sample or sampling location gives the first statistical level. With the average values for a variety of samples determined, the second statistical analysis involves the determination of the overall mean representing a geologic unit.

A statistical approach first worked out by Fisher has become the standard for analyzing the directions found in paleomagnetic studies. Each measurement is given unit weight and the mean position on the surface of a sphere determined, assuming that there is a gaussian-type distribution of points away from the mean. Using this approach, the mean declination and inclination for each sample is determined. In general, workers in the field use a 95-percent confidence level and calculate two statistical parameters. One of these is the radius of the cone of confidence, which is generally tabulated in paleomagnetic studies and gives a measure of the uncertainty of the direction determination. In addition, a precision parameter k that is a measure of the scatter of data points is commonly calculated. This parameter is 0 for a completely random set of directions, but it acquires large values of several hundred when the grouping of directions is good. Although no absolute criteria have been established for accepting or rejecting data, it is common to find that the radius of the circle of confidence is less than 20°, and the precision parameter is greater than 20. The advantage of using the precision parameter is that it is a normalized quantity and is not dependent upon the number of samples used in a study, provided of course, a sufficient number of samples is used and the scatter of directions is not too great. The precision parameter k is given as $(N-1)/(N-R)$, where N is the number of samples, and R is the sum of the individual vectors in the mean direction. When N is large, the expression reduces approximately to $N/(N-R)$, and it then becomes a true measure of the scatter of points. If the points are closely grouped, R approaches N so that the value of k is large, while if the data are highly scattered, R is small and the value of k is small.

When information is collected from a group of rocks, the NRM data are usually presented on a stereographic projection, which is the projection of a sphere into a horizontal plane. The inclination, or dip, below the horizon determined from the sample is given by the distance away from the edge of a circle, as shown in Fig. 5-1. The magnetic declination, or deviation from true north, determined from the sample is given by a line through the center of the circle. Thus a position on a stereographic projection represents a direction and completely defines the magnetic direction in the sample. The only ambiguity in plotting on a stereonet is to determine whether the magnetization is pointing up or down. To remove this ambiguity, different symbols are used. A typical stereographic projection is shown in Fig. 5-1, in which a set of typical data have been plotted. These

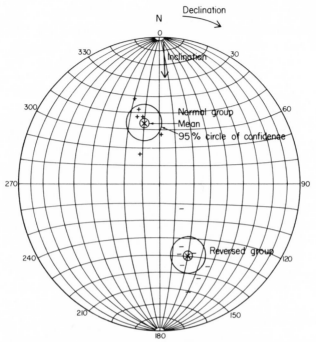

FIGURE 5-1   Schmidt stereographic projection showing a typical
set of data including normal and reversely magnetized samples.

+   normal, lower hemisphere.

—   reversed, upper hemisphere.

×   mean direction of groups shown; circle is
the 95-percent circle of confidence.

directions are from a group of flows from some very young rocks
and show typical normal and reverse magnetizations. The scatter
observed is typical of most observations in paleomagnetism.

Having determined the magnetic direction found in a
particular rock unit, it is possible to determine where a magnetic
pole corresponding to these directions is located. That is, a magnetic declination and inclination uniquely define a point on a
globe, just as a compass needle and a dip needle define a magnetic pole. If the earth's field were a simple dipole, this position
would be exactly the magnetic pole. If one looks at present-day

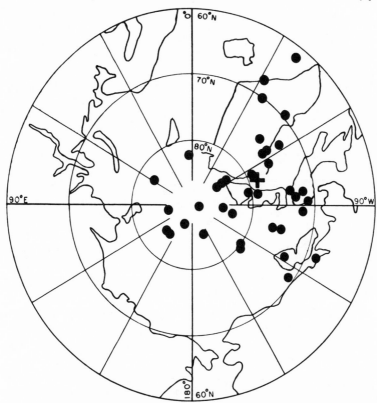

FIGURE 5-2   Virtual geomagnetic pole positions calculated from declination and inclination at present magnetic observatories (+ represents mean position) (from Doell et al., Paleomagnetism, vol. 8, Advances in Geophysics, Academic Press, Inc., New York, 1961).

observations and computes the "pole position" for each station, these positions fall at various distances (up to 20°) from the true dipolar magnetic pole (Fig. 5-2). When data from many stations are averaged, however, the mean position turns out to be truly the present magnetic pole. The variability shown here in pole position is that expected from the nondipole terms in the earth's field as it presently exists. At a single location if westward drift takes place, many such features would be sampled in sequence, and the scatter that we can expect is similar to this for any given observing point. It is necessary to average out this scatter in order to get meaningful paleomagnetic data. In principle, of course, one could also take observations from many parts of the world for rocks of precisely the same age and deduce the average of the magnetic field at that time. For practical reasons, it is much simpler to take a significant time average from one general area.

FIELD TESTS

Two major types of stability tests are available to us. One group of tests is known as *field tests*, in which we use the evidence from the rocks themselves, and the second is a group of *laboratory tests*. In much of paleomagnetism, the argument of self-consistency has been the dominant and most convincing argument for the stability of magnetization. The fact that a group of samples from a single geologic unit has the same direction of magnetization and that this direction deviates significantly from the present field is a substantial indication that the magnetization was not controlled by the present magnetic field. This fact over all others supports the idea that the magnetic direction in rock units does indeed reflect an ancient magnetic field. Unfortunately, it does not tell us that the magnetization detected was acquired at the time that the rock formed. Some subsequent process could either determine the direction of magnetization or bias it in some way. It is this problem more than most others that concerns paleomagnetists, and it is in this area that we may have difficulty in making full use of the results of paleomagnetism. Most of the field tests were devised by John Graham, and these tests where applicable are strong indicators of stability.

There are several tests: the fold test, the conglomerate test, the reversal test, and the contact test will be described.

the fold test

In many geologic situations folding has taken place since the rock originally formed in such a way that different parts of the same geologic unit are in different orientations. If the

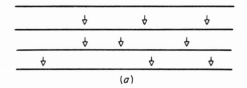

(a)

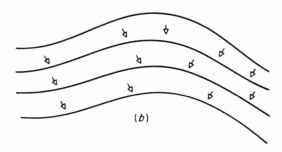

(b)

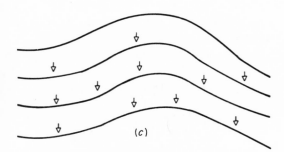

(c)

FIGURE 5-3   Illustrations of the fold test.
a   before folding.
b   after folding with only primary magnetization present.
c   after folding with secondary magnetization acquired after folding.

direction of magnetization was acquired before folding and if it is stable through geologic time, the present magnetizations on the two limbs of the fold will diverge. But when the limbs are fitted back into their original positions, as shown in Fig. 5-3, the directions of magnetization will coincide. This test is a very powerful one, and although it does not prove that secon-

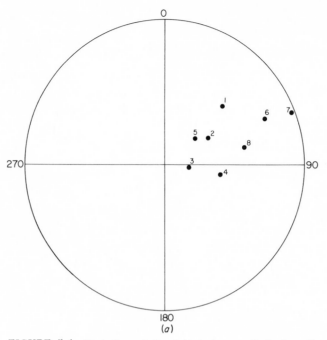

FIGURE 5-4   Illustration of the fold test on redbeds from the Rocky Mountains.

a   scatter in directions using present position of beds.

b   grouping of directions improved when correction is made for structure.

dary magnetization was not acquired before folding, it does prove that secondary magnetization has not been acquired in the time since folding. There are now many reported instances in the literature where the fold test has been applied, and it can be shown that a magnetization was acquired before folding and that it is stable and has not been altered since the time of folding.

One area in which such a test has been applied is in the study of redbeds in the Rocky Mountains. There, Permian beds of the same age with a variety of different structural orientations have been investigated. In some cases the present positions of the beds which were assumed in Cretaceous time are

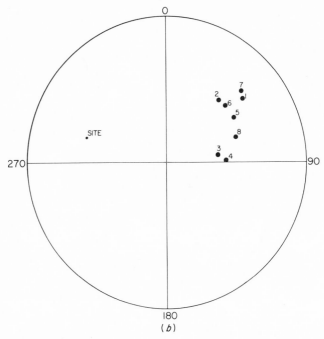

FIGURE 5-4   Continued.

almost vertical. The various directions when corrected to the original horizontal plane that the beds must have had, show a well-grouped set of magnetic directions (Fig. 5-4). In some cases where the fold test has been applied, it can be shown that a secondary magnetization has been acquired since folding. The evidence for this is that the same direction of magnetization is found on both limbs of the fold in their present position.

the conglomerate test

Another test of a similar nature is to look at conglomerates which have pebbles derived from an identifiable geologic unit. If the original rock has a stable magnetization, then the individual boulders in the conglomerate should also have a stable magnetization. Since the processes forming conglomerates are probably turbulent flash floods, the boulders tend to be randomly oriented and could not have had any magnetic control during

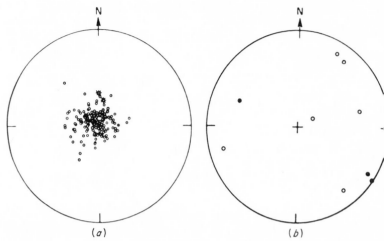

FIGURE 5-5   Illustration of the conglomerate test [from Irving, Paleomagnetism of the Narrabeen Chocolate Shales and the Tasmanian Dolerite, *J. Geophys. Res.*, **68**:2283–2287 (1963)].

a   Tasmanian dolerite showing good grouping

b   Breccia derived from the Tasmanian dolerite showing random scatter.

deposition. If the individual boulders have not been remagnetized since they were originally magnetized, they should have random orientations. In many cases when this test has been applied, the boulders have not been remagnetized since forming a conglomerate. That is, they still have a random orientation of magnetization. A typical set of data from a conglomerate showing random scattering as compared to the good grouping in the source rock is shown in Fig. 5-5. This type of evidence provides strong proof that viscous and chemical effects are not important in all rocks, even over periods as great as geologic time.

the reversal test

The evidence for reversals of the earth's magnetic field will be presented in the next chapter, but it is well established that the earth's field did reverse itself many times. Although we cannot be sure that the field reverses itself exactly, it seems likely that with the exclusion of secular variation this is the case. Accordingly, a group of data in which the reversal is about 180° is generally taken as evidence that the rocks involved have not acquired a magnetization since the time of formation. If the rock acquires a secondary magnetization, the effect would be to give an apparent reversal that was not exact. The reversal test is very useful, since it has a much more universal applicability than the previous tests, which require fairly rare geologic circumstances. At the same time, the test is not quite as strong, since it is not established that reversals need to be exactly 180° apart.

the baked-contact test

The last of the commonly used field tests is the study of baked-contact rocks. Intrusions of igneous rocks in nature are quite common, and the rocks which are intruded are reheated to some extent. This process will cause a remagnetization of the intruded rock as a result of cooling from above the Curie temperature. In general the magnetic minerals in the intrusion and in the rebaked rocks are different so that secondary processes are not likely to affect both formations in the same way. The result might be that one rock type could acquire a secondary magnetization more readily than the other, and given enough time the magnetic directions would tend to diverge. This is not generally found to be the case, and the agreement between the direction of magnetization of the intrusive rock and of the rebaked country rock nearby is usually very good.

There are several other ways of using field tests to test for stability, but these are of quite limited use and do not have general application. Tests of the type described are of extreme importance, for they provide the only means of testing the stability of magnetization over long periods of geologic time. They do not exclude the possibility of remagnetization completely, but the evidence is strong.

LABORATORY TESTS

There are many experiments that can be done in the laboratory to test the stability of magnetization and to remove secondary components of magnetization. These tests are also of considerable value, since they tend to remove unstable components of magnetization and permit the detection of the most stable fractions of the NRM. Looking at the stable fractions of NRM permits a sharpening of the paleomagnetic field tests already described. The tests that have found the most common usage are the alternating field demagnetization technique and the thermal demagnetization method. In addition, some workers test for viscous effects by storing the samples in various orientations with respect to the laboratory field. Any samples which change significantly in a matter of weeks or months are clearly unsuitable for paleomagnetism.

af demagnetization

The most universally applied laboratory test is the one which uses demagnetization in alternating magnetic fields. The technique is quite simple and involves exposing the sample to alternating magnetic fields of various strengths. In a rock with many different types of minerals and sites in which remanence can be carried, it is probable that the NRM does not have a single magnetic field which corresponds to the coercive force. Each sample has a bulk coercive force at which the magnetization is reduced to zero. However, the remanence can be divided into different portions with different coercive forces, so that there is a distribution of coercive forces, or a coercive-force spectrum. When placed in an alternating magnetic field, the portion of the magnetization whose coercive force is exceeded in the field will have its remanence randomized and therefore effectively removed. The result is that subjecting a sample to increasing magnetic fields causes different parts of the remanence to have the coercive force exceeded and therefore eliminated. As the field strengths become greater, the portions with the lower coercive forces are selectively removed, leaving only the most stable fractions of the NRM in the sample. In general, then, one chooses the af value which gives the best grouping of results without going to higher fields.

To illustrate this, the demagnetization curves of some typical rock specimens are illustrated in Fig. 5-6. For typical

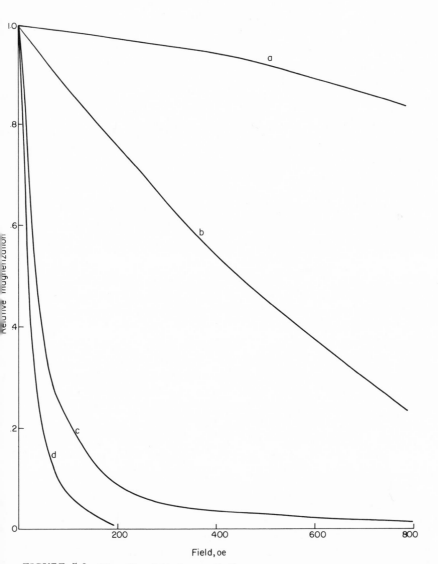

FIGURE 5-6   Alternating field demagnetization.

    a   redbed with hematite as the magnetic mineral.

    b   basalt with magnetite as the main magnetic mineral, broken up into small grains by exsolution.

    c   basalt with magnetite as the main magnetic mineral without exsolution so that grains are around 20 microns in size.

    d   granite with very large grains of magnetite.

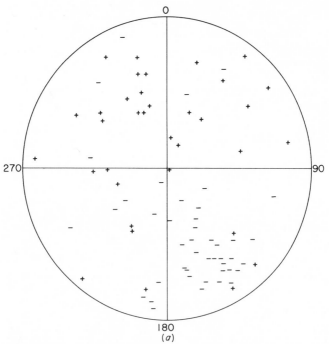

FIGURE 5-7   Effect of cleaning in alternating fields.
    a   before demagnetization.
    b   after demagnetization in fields of 200 oe.

volcanic rocks, it is seen that an appreciable remanent mag-netization is left even when fields as high as 1000 oe are used. This is a very high field compared with that of the earth and indicates that some of the NRM of typical volcanics is ex-tremely stable. Also shown is a curve for an "unstable" volcanic. This is the case of a volcanic rock in which the grains are quite large and subsequent cooling has not broken the grains up into smaller particles.

    Sediments can have a variety of af demagnetization characteristics, depending on the nature of the contained min-erals. Typical red sediments show extreme stability of magnetiza-tion, since in many cases the NRM is carried by hematite. In many cases this remanence is a partial thermoremanence ac-quired during reheating to 100 or 200°C after the chemical

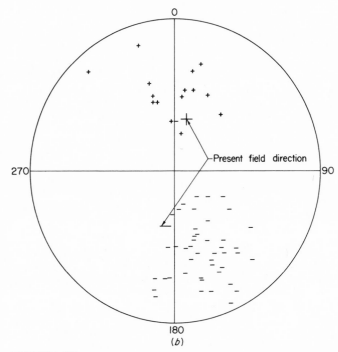

FIGURE 5-7   Continued.

changes which give rise to the hematite. Such reheatings could be associated with burial to a few thousand feet or with intrusive activity nearby. A typical curve for a red sediment is also given in Fig. 5-6, showing that at 1000 oe the NRM is hardly changed. Extremely high stability of this type is present only in rocks containing hematite, and hematite in red sediments is generally a secondary product.

A typical set of data showing the improvement in grouping of directions on af demagnetization is shown in Fig. 5-7. In this case demagnetization in fields of 200 oe removed less stable components of magnetization in random directions and left the most stable well-grouped directions.

thermal demagnetization

Another test that has found considerable favor is the process of thermal demagnetization. The procedure involves

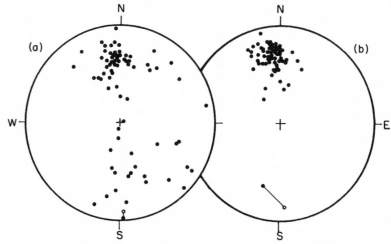

FIGURE 5-8   Effect of thermal cleaning on redbeds [from Irving and Opdyke, The Paleomagnetism of the Bloomsburg Redbeds and Its Possible Application to the Tectonic History of the Appalachians, *Geophys. J.* 9:153–167 (1965)].

heating samples to increasing temperatures and allowing them to cool in field-free space. This field-free space needs to be quite accurately adjusted so that the residual magnetic field is very small. If this is not done, various grains present can acquire a significant TRM which will obscure the NRM under study. This procedure has been quite effective in removing components of magnetization which are stable to af demagnetization, but which are still clearly secondary in origin. A study of the Old Red Sandstone of Devonian age, for example, shows that it has directions of magnetization that correspond to well-established Permian directions. When the unit was thermally demagnetized to 600°C, some of the NRM disappeared, and a typical Devonian field direction was found. The Old Red Sandstone thus apparently acquired a secondary magnetization long after its original formation. This secondary magnetization was stable to af demagnetization, but it could be removed by thermal demagnetization.

Thermal demagnetization is thus a powerful tool for removing secondary components of magnetization probably acquired as a result of partial reheatings late in the history of the rock. This technique appears to have special significance in the study of sedimentary rocks where secondary effects such as chemical changes are common, and the resulting magnetization is often hard to remove by af methods. Optimistically, much more of this work will be done in the future in order to sort out the problem of secondary effects. A typical example of thermal demagnetization is shown in Fig. 5-8.

There have been other techniques proposed for testing the stability and removal of unstable components. None of these has yet found widespread use. The overall problem of detecting secondary magnetizations is one of the most serious ones facing paleomagnetism at present, and undoubtedly there will be many advances in this field.

6

paleointensity

In addition to the direction of the earth's magnetic field, it is also possible in principle to determine the strength of the field at various times in the past. At the time of writing, only a small amount of data are available, but certain features are beginning to emerge. The main problem in determining the paleointensity is to reproduce in the laboratory the conditions under which the magnetization originally formed. Viscous and chemical effects after the original magnetization process are clearly undesirable and to be avoided at all costs. To date most work has been concentrated on baked potteries and bricks of archaeological interest and on igneous rocks, primarily volcanic, since the magnetization process is fairly well understood. In both cases it appears that TRM is the dominant mechanism for generation of the remanence being measured. We have already discussed the acquisition of TRM and shown that for the weak fields found in nature there is a good proportionality between the total TRM and the field.

The earliest efforts at determining the value of the ancient field were thus simply done by heating samples to above their Curie temperatures and allowing them to acquire a TRM in a known field. The value of the ancient field is then given by $H_{ancient} = H_{known} (NRM)/(TRM)$. This approach was used to a limited degree, but it was soon found to be dangerous, because it had no built-in checks. Heating of rocks and minerals to 600 or 700°C can cause extensive changes in the magnetic minerals and hence in the magnetization. Measurement of the total TRM in this way is therefore no guarantee that there is an equivalence between the NRM in the rock and the TRM created in the laboratory. Rather, much more comprehensive testing procedures need to be used in order to insure that reheating in the laboratory does not change the characteristics.

The classical work in paleointensity was done by the Thelliers, working in Paris. They have thoroughly documented a set of tests that determine the suitability of a rock or pottery specimen and thus the ancient intensity. Most of their work has been concentrated on baked bricks and potteries of known archaeological age, generally limited to the last 2000 years. The Thellier approach to intensity determination is briefly outlined here, since it is the basic standard used by all workers in this field. Use is made of the principle of PTRM, which states that the TRM acquired in any given temperature interval is independent of that acquired in other temperature intervals. Each PTRM thus preserves information about the intensity independent of the rest of the TRM so that one can make several estimates of the intensity. In the simplified procedure, one heats the samples to a given temperature and allows them to cool in a field-free space. This causes the loss of a small portion of the NRM. The sample is then reheated to the same temperature and allowed to cool in a known field. The amount of magnetization acquired in this way represents the TRM acquired in that temperature interval. The ancient-field intensity is then given as above by taking the ratio of the NRM to the TRM. The procedure is then repeated at increasing temperatures, and the ratio is taken. The data obtained in this way are similar to those shown in Fig. 6-1, showing a plot of the magnetization acquired in a known field versus the magnetization lost by cooling in field-free space.

A curve such as the one shown in Fig. 6-1 must yield a straight line in order that the sample be useful for intensity determinations. Deviations from a straight-line behavior could be due to chemical changes during heating. Other possible effects, such as a change in the proportionality between the intensity acquired and the applied field as a function of temperature,

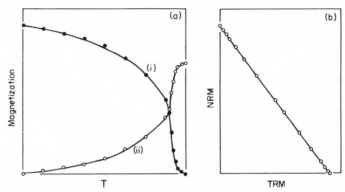

FIGURE 6-1   *a*   (i)   Plot showing loss of NRM on heating to temperature shown and cooling in field-free space.
(ii)   Plot showing TRM acquired by heating to temperature shown and cooling in the earth's field.
b   Plot of NRM remaining after cooling in field-free space versus TRM acquired by cooling in a known field. Each point corresponds to a different temperature. Slope of this line gives ratio of ancient and modern fields.

might also be important. Many samples show a reasonably good straight-line relationship up to temperatures near the Curie temperature, which indicates that these samples are suitable for paleointensity studies.

The full Thellier test involves determining the loss of NRM and acquisition of TRM in limited temperature intervals such as 100 to 200°C, 200 to 300°C, etc., up to the Curie temperature, as just discussed. However, after heating to higher temperatures, such as the 300 to 400°C interval, the whole set of data for lower-temperature intervals is redetermined—in the 100 to 200°C interval and the 200 to 300°C interval—to insure that no mineralogic changes have taken place. This procedure is very time-consuming, but the comparison of data from various temperature intervals and the repeat checks after each heating are very strong assurances that samples which give the same repeatable value of intensity are in fact giving the right answer. Needless to say, few investigations have been conducted with such rigor.

Abbreviated versions of these procedures have been used by many workers to give values of intensity. Archaeological data have been the most comprehensively studied, and these results will be discussed in some detail in Chap. 7. In the past 2000 years the field appears to have decreased somewhat, but in general the earth's dipole moment has ranged between 7 and 15×10^{25} gauss cm^3. The present value is 8.06×10^{25}. This range in amplitude is fairly limited.

Other simplified procedures have been used at various times by other workers. Perhaps the most useful of these is the matching of af demagnetization curves. This procedure has the distinct advantage of eliminating possible effects due to viscous magnetization by looking only at those parts of the curves which are stable to af demagnetization in fields of 500 oe or greater. The procedure is illustrated in Fig. 6-2. The demagnetization curve of the NRM is plotted. The sample is then heated to 600°C and allowed to cool in the earth's field and the curve for the demagnetization of the TRM is plotted. The ratio of the ancient field to the modern field is given by the ratio which makes the high-stability ends of the curves meet. The procedure is repeated after heating at 700 and 800°C. If the TRM curve changes significantly between 600 and 800°C, it indicates that the sample is subject to change on heating and should be rejected.

In general those samples which are initially highly oxidized are most amenable to this treatment, since heating causes little further change. Those samples which are initially unoxidized, however, develop extensive lamellae and the magnetization changes greatly above 600°C due to the formation of small particles. This approach to paleointensity specifically detects viscous effects by demagnetization and mineral changes that affect the magnetic properties on heating.

The comparison of paleointensity results requires a reduction to a common latitude. The procedure involved is not entirely suitable, for it requires knowing the inclination of a site exactly and ignoring secular variation. As we have already seen, this leads to errors of about 20° in direction, and the local magnetic field strength at any time can deviate by 20 per-

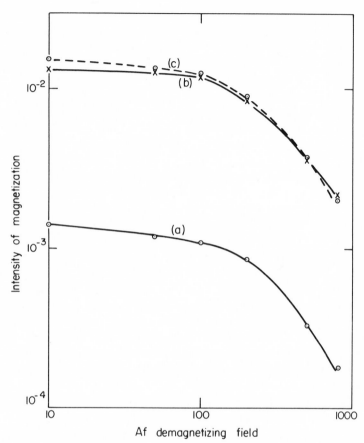

FIGURE 6-2 Determination of Paleointensity by matching af demagnetization curves.

a NRM.

b TRM acquired by cooling from 600°C in a known field.

c NRM values multiplied by a constant factor to match
TRM and NRM curves at fields of 500 and 1000 oe.
Deviation at lower field strengths is probably due to
viscous effects.

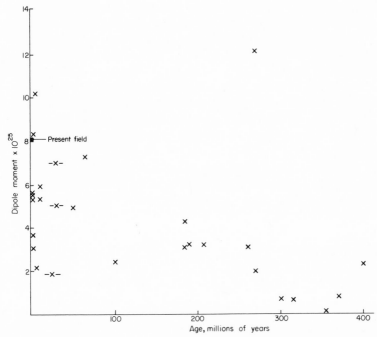

FIGURE 6-3 Plot of magnetic dipole moment of the earth as a function of geologic time.

cent or more from the mean dipole field. For simplicity of comparing results, it is usual to reduce them to an equivalent equator, assuming the field to be dipolar. As a first-order reduction, this procedure is certainly adequate. The dipolar field expression $F_{eq} = F/(1 + 3 \cos \theta)^{1/2}$ is generally used, where θ is the colatitude, and F_{eq} is the equatorial field. This allows a comparison of results between observing sites in a general way.

In view of the secular variation which has been discussed in Chap. 5, it seems probable that over a period of a few thousand years each observing site could have its own variations in intensity, with ranges up to 20 percent due to secular change alone. There is therefore some difficulty in determining the mean dipole moment of the earth at any given time in the past without doing averaging in the same manner as is done for directional data. To date far too few determinations have been made to permit rigorous statistical tests to be applied.

A recent compilation of available data by Smith gives the pattern shown in Fig. 6-3. This shows that the field over the last few million years is close to the present value with considerable fluctuations. In older rocks of Permian, Carboniferous, and Devonian age, the field appears to have been much weaker than at present. This same conclusion was reached in 1938 by Koenigsberger who worked on rocks of varying ages.

7

archaeomagnetism: the last 2000 years

Archaeologists are slowly piecing together the history of man and his evolution during the past few thousand years. During this same period of time, the magnetic field of the earth has been changing due to secular variation. The study of the changes during this time is called *archaeomagnetism*. Some of the main relics that archaeologists have been able to use are baked potteries and other baked objects which survive through the ages. Fortunately, these objects are often made of clay which contains some iron materials. When heated, the iron minerals convert to hematite, and on cooling they acquire a stable TRM. The TRM acquired reflects the earth's field at the time of last baking of the objects.

The objects that have been particularly useful in archaeomagnetism are pots, bricks, old fireplace hearths, and kilns. In the first two cases it is possible to determine only the dip of the field and not the declination, since bricks and pots are usually baked in an upright position; they are, of course, subsequently moved around and used in building or for other purposes. In the case of old fireplaces and old brick kilns, on the other hand, it is possible to recover the complete direction of the earth's magnetic field at the location, since the material has not been moved since firing. The work of reconstructing the changes in direction of the field over the last few thousand years is very tedious and time-consuming, but the results are very important to our understanding of the magnetic record. Data acquired in this way form a supplement to the meager observatory records available for a few hundred years. The studies to date have been concentrated in areas where the archaeology has been intensively studied and many useful artifacts are available. Early studies in this field were conducted by Prof. Thellier and his coworkers, and since then many other laboratories have started similar studies. Active centers of this type of research are now to be found in Japan, the United States, England, Russia, and Czechoslovakia.

It is not yet possible to make detailed comparisons of these data, since many of them remain unpublished. However, some data are available which show many interesting features of the earth's magnetic field in recent history.

SECULAR VARIATION IN DIRECTION

We have already discussed secular variation as it is recorded at observatories. Archaeomagnetism provides us with a means of studying these processes for longer time periods as well as providing data for regions where the historical record is very short. Some of the data that have been compiled to date are given in Fig. 7-1, where the pole position corresponding to the measured declination and inclination is given. The most striking and intriguing feature of the data is that for the areas so far studied in detail, the apparent pole position appears to wander in a definite pattern with typical excursions from the north pole of up to 20°. The average position over about 1000 years, however, appears to come close to giving the rotation pole of the earth. Apparently, the present discrepancy between the magnetic dipole axis and the rotation axis is a passing phenomenon, and a period of about 2000 years is sufficient to average out these effects. This motion is referred to as the *apparent pole position,* since it is not possible to determine whether these variations are due to changes in the main field of the earth or whether in fact they represent local events and preserve a record of

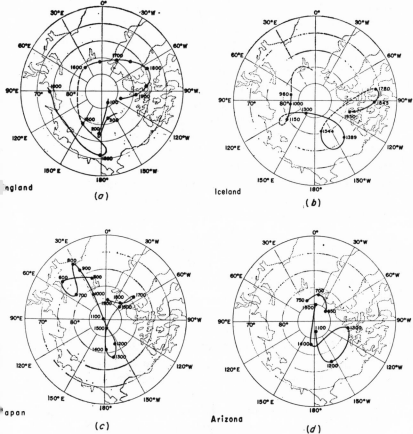

FIGURE 7-1   Apparent pole positions for archaeomagnetic data [from Kawai, Hirooka, and Sasajima, Counterclockwise Rotation of the Geomagnetic Dipole Axis Revealed in World-wide Archaeosecular Variation, *Proc. Japan Acad.*, 41:398–403 (1965)].

a   England.
b   Iceland.
c   Japan.
d   southwestern U.S.A.

the secular variation at the general sampling area similar to that shown in observatory records. It is certain that if the main dipole of the earth can wobble, variations in apparent pole position should be simultaneous the world over. If, on the other hand, the variations in apparent pole position are due to secular variations, widely separated parts of the earth should show different polar paths. In Fig. 7-1 the patterns shown do not give an unambiguous interpretation. The apparent pole paths followed could be due to a wobbling of the main dipole in a counterclockwise sense with a superimposed local effect giving the smaller variations as suggested by Kawai. If, on the other hand, the archaeomagnetic variations are the result of secular variation alone, then we must acknowledge that eastward drift has taken place, as shown by the small loops in Fig. 7-1, so that the present-day westward drift is merely a passing stage in the earth's magnetic field. Unfortunately, it will require very detailed studies in order to completely settle this controversy, since the data available to date suggest that all areas have gross similarities in the apparent pole position with smaller variations among them.

In spite of uncertainties in the data, the records preserved in the archaeological record can be interpreted as secular variation; thus, it seems that to get a true mean pole position, it is necessary to average data over a considerable length of time—at least 2000 years. If all the presently available archaeomagnetic data were averaged, the result would be a pole position close to the present rotation pole. It appears, therefore, that in a period of 2000 years, the average position of the magnetic pole of the earth coincides with the rotation pole, while at present it is 11° away from the rotation pole.

The archaeological record then leads us to the following conclusions:

1   Both westward drift and apparent eastward drift occur.
2   The nature of secular variation has been relatively the same for the last 2000 years.
3   The mean of the available poles indicates that the present rotation pole of the earth corresponds to the mean geomagnetic pole for the last 2000 years. This means (*a*)

that 2000 years of time-averaging of the field at a single location is sufficient to average out secular variation and (b) that the geomagnetic pole is very closely coupled to the rotation pole.

SECULAR VARIATION IN INTENSITY

The second type of information that can be derived from archaeological artifacts is the strength of the ancient magnetic field. The work involved in conducting these experiments is considerable, as discussed in Chap. 6, and in the process many samples are found to be unsuitable for paleointensity studies. The main difficulty as already discussed is that the minerals may change on heating and the effects on the magnetization can be very subtle so that extensive precautionary measures need to be taken.

Nevertheless, some data from Japan, France, Russia, and the southwestern United States have been published. These are summarized in Fig. 7-2. It is readily seen that the intensity values are variable and show a wide range of values. In spite of this, a general trend in all the data indicates that the strength of the magnetic field has decreased steadily in the past 2000 years. Once again, it will be extremely important to study these variations at different places on the globe. If the changes in field strength were significantly different at different places, it would indicate that local secular variation was being observed. On the other hand, if the intensity values from different parts of the world are similar, this would support the concept that the field is generally dipolar in character and that it is the dipole itself that is changing in strength.

Using observatory records as already discussed, it has been shown that the dipole moment of the earth decreased from a value of 8.55×10^{25} emu in 1835 to 8.06×10^{25} emu in 1955. This decrease is substantial and is related to a weakening of the overall field rather than to local secular patterns. Considering only a single observing point, fluctuations up to 50 percent in the field can be expected, as shown on maps of secular variation. At the present time the nondipole terms of the earth's magnetic

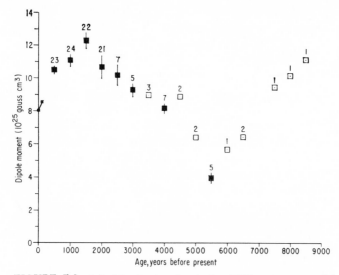

FIGURE 7-2   Paleointensity data for the last 2000 years—equatorial field (numbers refer to number of samples) [from Cox, Length of Geomagnetic Polarity Intervals, *J. Geophys. Res.*, **73**:3247–3260 (1968)].

field show typical variations on the earth's surface up to about 0.2 oe. Since the earth's main dipole field varies from 0.3 oe at the equator to 0.6 oe at the poles, this means that local variation up to 50 percent or more of the field strength can occur. In view of this it is not surprising that the paleointensity data shown in Fig. 7-2 have the indicated scatter. This variation is about what we might expect if we should examine the present field. The rms secular variation rate is about 50 γ/year. If the sense of this persisted at one place for about 500 years in one direction, the intensity at one spot could change by about 0.25 oe. One might expect, then, to see considerable scatter at any one observing area, but if many observing locations show the same pattern, it is likely to be a property of the main dipole.

If we consider a typical center of secular variation and how we might expect the declination, inclination, and field strength to change, the type of behavior expected is as shown in Fig. 7-3. The declination should change sign as the nondipole

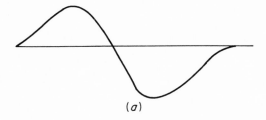

(a)

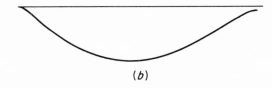

(b)

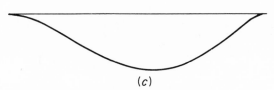

(c)

FIGURE 7-3   Expected time variation associated with
centers of secular variation.
a   declination.
b   inclination.
c   intensity.

part of the field passes the station, while the inclination and
intensity should show a similar behavior. If patterns of this
sort are found, it will be clear that the secular variation accounts
for the main apparent polar wandering over the last few thousand years. On the other hand, if there is no correlation between

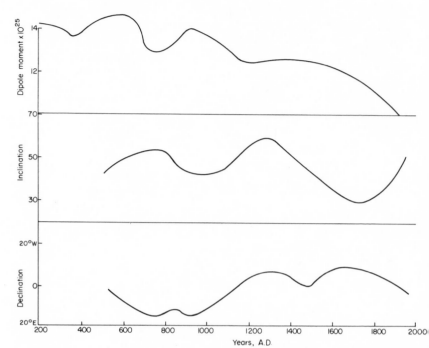

FIGURE 7-4   Observed changes in declination, inclination, and equatorial dipole moment for data from Japan [from Kawai, Hirooka, Sasajima, Ito, Yaskawa, and Kume, Archaeomagnetic Studies in Southwestern Japan, *Ann. Geophys.*, **21**:574–578 (1965)].

the intensity of the field variations and the direction changes, then it seems probable that a larger term affecting the main dipole field strength is present. Only from Japan are sufficient data available to test this. The data available are given in Fig. 7-4, where it can be seen that no real correlation between direction and intensity variations is evident. Rather, it appears that the field strength of the main dipole is simply decreasing. This is supported by the evidence that the field in different parts of the world has decreased in a similar way and by the fact that it is known to have decreased in the past 100 years.

It is, of course, interesting to speculate on whether the

field which is decreasing steadily now will continue to decrease. If it does so at the same rate as it is now decreasing, the field will be reduced to zero in about 2000 years. It is certainly possible that we are approaching a reversal of the field since it is the main dipole that appears to be decreasing. The consequences of this will be discussed in the next chapter.

8

reversals of the earth's magnetic field

One of the most exciting discoveries about the ancient magnetic field is that it has reversed itself at frequent intervals in the geologic past. It was recognized in the very earliest studies of the magnetic properties of volcanic rocks that many geologic units had a magnetic remanence in them that was roughly opposed to the present field direction. Even at that time it was speculated that this was an indication that the earth's field had been reversed at some time in the past. As studies of the polarity of the magnetic vector in rocks have continued, it has been found that approximately half of all rocks are reversely magnetized, indicating that the earth's magnetic polarity has changed many times in the earth's history. Neel, making theoretical studies of ferrite materials, predicted that some materials might show the property of self-reversal, whereby the TRM acquired could be opposed to the applied field. This opened the possibility that the reversed magnetism represented not reversals in the field but some property of the material.

SELF-REVERSALS

It is therefore important to study in detail, mechanisms by which the magnetic moment of rocks could show such a spontaneous reversal. We have already seen that the magnetic minerals are generally ferrimagnetic or antiferromagnetic so that there are inverse internal fields present. Complete self-reversal was discussed in connection with the properties of the ilmenite-hematite series of minerals. In this case it was found that for a limited composition range the spontaneous TRM acquired on cooling to room temperature is reversed. This is due to the inter-action of two ferrite sublattices in which there is negative ex-change coupling. The first lattice to be magnetized on cooling is aligned in the applied field. The second lattice to be mag-netized is controlled by the first one and becomes reversely magnetized. In all ferrites there is such a reversely magnetized sublattice, but in only a few cases does this magnetization exceed that of the normally magnetized sublattice. To date, only a few artificial materials and the ilmenite-hematite series among natu-ral minerals are known to have this property. Neel, however, postulated a second group of effects which would not be de-tectable in laboratory tests, since they involve the decay of the magnetization or chemical changes of only one of the sublattices. The normally magnetized sublattice would dominate at the time of acquisition of the TRM, but after enough time had passed the magnetization of this sublattice would decay, leaving the reversely magnetized sublattice to contribute the dominant rema-nence. This effect is then a self-reversal process, but the evidence in nature is largely destroyed due to the irreversible nature of the mechanism. For this reason this type of reversal could not be detected in laboratory tests.

The only way to test the possibility that self-reversals of this kind have taken place in nature is to search for a correla-tion between the magnetic polarity and some property of the minerals which carry the magnetization. This has been done in many different studies, but no clear correlation has been found. Some workers have reported that reversely magnetized rocks tend to have high states of oxidation. As discussed in connection with magnetic minerals, this means that much high-temperature exsolution has taken place as part of the cooling process, leading to a very stable TRM in reversely magnetized units. Since these studies, however, many highly oxidized normal rocks and many poorly oxidized reversed rocks have been found, so that the correlation is not universal. Moreover, the oxidation state in a single lava flow varies greatly from portions that are quite unoxidized to portions that are highly oxidized so that one geologic unit cannot even be classified in this way.

If continued studies show that no differences can be found between reversely magnetized and normally magnetized bodies, the only meaningful test of self-reversal will be to find a single body which has both polarities in it. If examples of this type could be found in which the correct sense of the polarity at the time of cooling could be determined (say by a baked-contact test), it might be possible to find a meaningful correlation between the petrology of the magnetic minerals and the self-reversal. To date, no cases are known in which there is clear-cut field evidence showing self-reversals, except in rocks containing ilmeno-hematites. Needless to say, we must be prepared to continue the investigation.

FIELD REVERSALS

In contrast to the search for self-reversals in nature, much evidence has been produced to show that the field did in fact reverse. The most convincing evidence of all has been produced by the combined study of paleomagnetism and careful isotopic age-dating, since basaltic rocks have been found to have sufficient potassium to be suitable for potassium-argon dating. In very young rocks, less than about 5 million years old, many investigators have found consistent evidence on a worldwide basis to show that reversals take place simultaneously around the world. This evidence is strong proof that field reversals do occur, since many different basalt types and areas show consistent results. In Fig. 8-1, a chart showing the identified polarity sequence is given. This includes data from many places and several laboratories, and although additional features may yet appear, the general sequence of events for the last 5 million years is now clear.

Several long periods of 1×10^6 years or so, in which the polarity of the field remained fairly consistent, can be seen

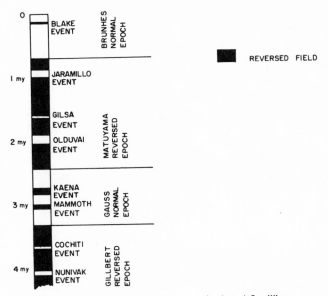

REVERSED FIELD

FIGURE 8-1 Reversal sequence during the last 4.5 million years.

in Fig. 8-1. Superimposed on this simple pattern is a series of much shorter, almost transient, reversals which have been called *events*. These events are so short that it is difficult to be certain of their duration and to be sure that others do not exist. Statistical considerations indicate that they last for somewhere between 10,000 and 100,000 years. In the future, as more rocks are studied, we can expect to find that there are more events which have been overlooked.

TRANSITION ZONES

It is difficult to estimate the length of time required for a reversal to take place. Again, however, statistical considerations indicate that the actual reversing time is typically less than 5000 years, since most rocks are either normally or reversely magnetized. Only a few sequences of lava flows have been found which show intermediate directions likely to indicate transitional directions. Detailed studies of such zones have been reported

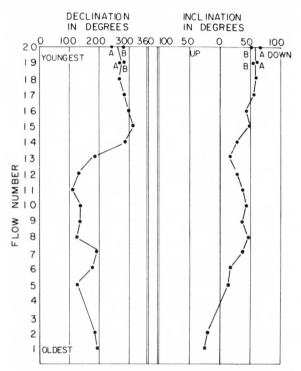

FIGURE 8-2 Change in declination and inclination in a Tertiary magnetic transition for southeastern Oregon [from Goldstein, Larson, and Strangway, Paleomagnetism of a Miocene Transition Zone in Southeastern Oregon, *Earth Planet. Sci. Lett.*, 1:(1969)].

from the U.S.S.R., South Africa, Japan, and the United States. In Fig. 8-2, the declination and inclination found in successive lavas in a sequence of lava flows from southeastern Oregon is shown. The age of this transition zone is 15.1 million years. In Fig. 8-2, it is seen that the direction of the magnetic field appears to swing in a fairly smooth pattern from normal to reverse. Patterns of this sort can be traced in volcanic sequences for a hundred miles or more, and they are found to be similar; however, until we can make detailed comparisons between the intermediate directions found in different parts of the world

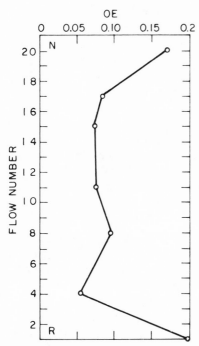

FIGURE 8-3   Intensity changes in the
transition zone shown in
Fig. 8-3 (same source as
Fig. 8-2).

for the same transition zone, we will not be able to reconstruct the nature of the overall field during the transition.

It will be interesting to determine whether the field collapses to a very small value and then builds up in the opposite sense or whether it remains a dipole field and then merely tilts over. Unfortunately, very few clearcut transition zones are available for study, and even when they are, the lava flows that represent them are usually quite few in number so that adequate and detailed sampling is not possible. One useful approach to transition zones is to measure the strength of the magnetic field using the methods described in Chap. 6. This has been done for some of the transition zones that have been studied in detail. Figure 8-3 shows values of the field during the direction changes of Fig. 8-2. The strength of the field drops quite markedly down to a low value of 0.07 oe. This is a factor of 3 less than values found above and below the zone, and in fact samples from a nearby area have values as high as 0.5 oe. The range of field shown is roughly a factor of 10, indicating a great weakening of the field strength during the reversal.

CONTACT TEST FOR FIELD REVERSAL

There are various lines of evidence which are used to support the fact that field reversals are real. One of the more intriguing of these is the use of the baked-contact test. In this test, detailed paleomagnetic studies are made of the direction of magnetization in an igneous body and in the nearby rocks that have been rebaked by the igneous rocks. If self-reversal were a common occurrence, one would expect to find that in some cases the mineralogy in either the igneous body or that in the rebaked body would be such as to allow self-reversals. In that event, the main body and the rebaked rock could have opposite polarities. In about 95 percent of all cases examined to date, the igneous body and the baked contact have the same polarity. This then is another powerful test that supports field reversals and indicates that self-reversals are uncommon in nature.

SEA-FLOOR SEDIMENTS AND REVERSALS

As further support of the reversal of the earth's field, oceanographers have been making detailed studies of cores collected from the sea floor. The rate of sedimentation is believed to be fairly uniform, and there are no large gaps in the sedimentary record during the last few million years. The magnetism of these claylike muds is weak, and is not exceedingly stable, and the material is soft and difficult to handle. However, careful studies of such material have shown that there is a consistent record of polarity preserved in the sediments. Undoubtedly the magnetization is a simple DRM due to the settling of fine particles of magnetite or maghemite, although the detailed mineral-

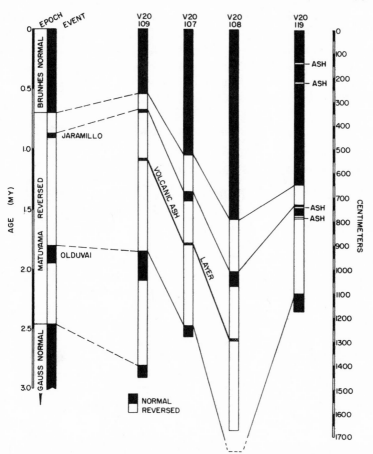

FIGURE 8-4   Magnetic polarity logs for deep-sea cores from the North Pacific. Note location of ash beds [from Ninkovich, Opdyke, Heezen, and Foster, Paleomagnetic Stratigraphy, Rates of Deposition and Tephrachronology in North Pacific Deep-sea Sediments, *Earth Planet. Sci. Lett.*, 1:476 (1966)].

ogy is unknown. Data such as those shown in Fig. 8-4 indicate that a definite sequence of reversals is present. If one assumes that the first reversal found nearest the top of the core is the most recent reversal found in land volcanics (700,000 years), it is possible to assign a rate of sedimentation. This rate can then be extrapolated back in time. If the sedimentation rate is uniform, the reversals found should correspond to those detected in volcanics. The agreement found in most cases is striking. Since the process of magnetization is probably DRM and the volcanics on land are magnetized by TRM, two completely different mechanisms of magnetization yield the same pattern of reversals. This has been one of the more conclusive pieces of evidence supporting reversals of the field.

REVERSAL TIMES AND RATES

There is little doubt that the earth's magnetic field has reversed itself many times in the geologic past, and therefore it is reasonable to inquire whether there is a characteristic reversal pattern with certain key frequencies or whether the pattern of reversals is random with time. It is not yet possible to answer the question completely, and it could be that the details of reversal sequences in some portions of the geologic record will never be fully unraveled. There are certain features, however, which do appear to be established characteristics. The last 5 or 6 million years of geologic time, for example, are well documented by independent means. It is striking that the short events with lifetimes of 10,000 to 100,000 years are so common in the pattern. It has been pointed out by Prof. Hide that such short-lived phenomena could be related to things happening in the core, since no other part of the earth's interior has time scales of motion likely to impress such rapid changes. On the other hand, there are periods of one polarity or the other which have typical lifetimes of a million or more years. These reversals have time scales more nearly comparable to the time scale required for geologic processes. It is an intriguing suggestion that these may be forced reversals, impressed upon the core by processes taking place in the mantle. Perhaps a slight modification of the core-mantle boundary, for example, could have drastic effects on the fluid-core motion, which could go so far as to initiate a reversal.

If we consider other geologic times, the reversal pattern is not nearly so clear, since the dating precision becomes too

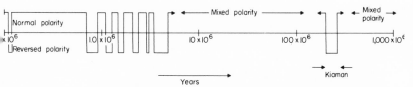

FIGURE 8-5   Reversal sequence in geologic history showing Kiaman interval (approx. Permian) [from McMahon and Strangway, Kiaman Magnetic Interval in the Western United States, *Science*, 155 (3765), 1012–1013 (1967)]. Copyright, 1967, American Association for the Advancement of Science.

poor to put isolated volcanic rocks in their correct sequence, and we have few continuous records in geology to work with. Consequently, paleomagnetic data have generally been lumped together for recognizable geologic time boundaries, and little or no account has been taken of the details of the reversal patterns within these units. It seems now to be well established that the reversal pattern during most of the Tertiary (last 70 my) was quite similar to that of the last 5 or 6 million years, in which reversals were very frequent. There are other periods, however, when the reversal pattern was quite different. One of these corresponds roughly to the Permian period (225 to 270 my), a period of about 45 million years, where all paleomagnetic data studied so far have but a single polarity. The record from Europe, North America, and Australia has been particularly useful in elucidating this, and again igneous and sedimentary rocks both show the constant reversed polarity.

The generalized information available is given in Fig. 8-5, in which it is seen that the beginning of the interval was probably in the late Pennsylvanian and that it continued until the Lower Triassic. The boundaries of the interval are sufficiently well defined that it can be used as a geologic time marker for long-range stratigraphic correlation. The only exception to the consistent reversal has been recorded in the Russian literature on upper Permian beds. The evidence at hand does not yet indicate whether there was indeed a normal time in the upper Permian period or whether there has been difficulty in correlating the fossil record on the two sides of the Iron Curtain.

In either case, there is little doubt that the Permian period was one in which the magnetic field was dominantly reversed. Short-lived reversals may be found in the future in rocks of this age, but the chances of this are being steadily reduced.

This, of course, has interesting implications in support of the reality of field reversals as opposed to self-reversals. If the reversely magnetized rocks that have been found to date were due to self-reversal mechanism, it would be necessary to conclude that all Permian rocks were self-reversing, whereas in other time intervals only about 50 percent of them were self-reversed. This seems so unlikely that this argument can be added to the lines of evidence against self-reversal.

Other portions of the geologic column are likely to be found with characteristic reversal patterns. Thus, it has already been noted that in the Triassic immediately after the close of the Kiaman, the field reversed itself very rapidly, perhaps as frequently as it has in the past 5 or 6 million years. Rocks of late Cretaceous age (perhaps including lower Tertiary), on the other hand, appear to have been dominantly normally magnetized. Future studies will undoubtedly reveal many more details about the reversal sequence at different times in the earth's history.

POSSIBLE CAUSES OF REVERSALS

The problem of the origin of reversals is a very difficult one, since, as we have just seen, the earth's field appears to reverse itself frequently but with no set periodicity. Rather, it is an irregular process, but as nearly as can be determined the field reverses itself by almost exactly 180°. In the generating mechanism of the field, this condition is one of the important restraints that will need to be explained by any full model for the mechanism creating the field.

The mechanism of the reversal is so far explained only by the observation that the models of a homogenous dynamo are not sensitive to the polarity of the field. Either polarity is equally acceptable, provided the magnetic field is coupled to the rotation axis. Hide has suggested that there may be free reversals associated with processes of entirely internal origin within the core as well as forced reversals impressed in some way by processes external to the core. It may well be that the complicated eddy motions in the core can lead to systems coupled in a nonlinear manner so that the whole poloidal field is quite unstable. It is clear that most of the magnetic energy is tied up in the large toroidal field, and small oscillations could lead to complete reversals of the small field we observe at the surface, without involving large amounts of energy.

If indeed there are forced reversals in the magnetic field, one needs to think about possible mechanisms that might generate these changes. It has been suggested that small irregularities on the core-mantle boundary (say, 1 km) extending over large areas could have an important influence on the magnetohydrodynamic conditions within the core. Slight changes in this might lead to profound changes in the magnetohydrodynamic regime of this rotating fluid. In this case, anything that could modify the core-mantle boundary could be of importance. Perhaps convective motion in the lower mantle could slightly modify the boundary and impress a forced reversal.

POSSIBLE EFFECTS OF REVERSALS ON LIFE

Several authors have considered the possibility that the removal of the magnetic field would remove the shielding effect of the Van Allen radiation belt, and the surface of the earth would be exposed to greater fluxes of cosmic rays during the reversal. This greater cosmic ray flux, it is argued, would lead to serious effects on mutation rates or on evolution. It is useful to consider this problem in some detail, since it could have important consequences on evolutionary theory. During times of many reversals, evolutionary rates might be distinctly higher than during times of few reversals. Unfortunately, the evidence from paleontology is difficult to put on a numerical basis, and it is difficult to draw meaningful conclusions about correlations.

The atmosphere is a much stronger absorber of cosmic-ray particles than the magnetic field so that the difference in total cosmic ray flux at the earth's surface in the presence or absence of a magnetic field is likely to be very small. The direct effect on life is likely therefore to be small. There is, of course, the possibility that the indirect effect could be significant. Particles which would normally be trapped by the field and not interact with the atmosphere might penetrate more deeply into the atmosphere and create many more radioactive daughter products. These products in turn might reach the earth's surface and be absorbed by living creatures.

As a test of this, detailed correlations of the microscopic fossils found in the sea-floor sediments have been made. Paleontologists have been able to trace the presence of various faunal horizons and the length of time they existed. In general, there is a rough agreement between the extinction of a faunal type and reversals. The evidence cannot be interpreted unequivocally, however, since the faunal types were presumably undergoing some type of evolution in any case. It must be concluded that it seems most unlikely that any real cause and effect of this type will be found, but much additional evidence is needed. It has been suggested, for example, that climatic conditions might be quite different in times of polarity changes, causing changes in the fossil record.

SEA-FLOOR SPREADING

Perhaps the most exciting consequences of discoveries of reversals in the earth's magnetic field have been the surprising implications that can be drawn about the sea floor. It has long been known that when airborne or shipborne magnetometers are used to map the nature of the magnetic field at sea, large fluctuations occur. These have always been taken to indicate that the sea floor is composed mainly of highly magnetic volcanic rocks. The exciting discoveries are that these features have long linear trends which run roughly parallel to the great midocean ridge system. Moreover, when the peaks and troughs of the magnetic profiles are examined in detail they show symmetry about the axis of the midocean ridge, as shown in Fig. 8-6, taken from a paper by Heirtzler and coworkers of the Lamont Geological Observatory. A symmetry of this sort

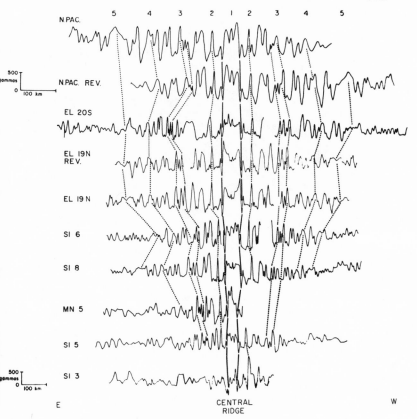

FIGURE 8-6   Magnetic anomaly profiles from the North Pacific. Dashed lines connect corresponding anomalies on the profiles (anomalies 1–5). The central ridge axis is outlined with solid lines (anomaly 1). The top two profiles are the same profile, but the second one is reversed to show the striking symmetry about the central anomaly. Remaining profiles are in sequence from north to south. Numbers refer to the ship cruise [from Pitman, Herron, and Heirtzler, Magnetic Anomalies in the Pacific and Sea-floor Spreading. *J. Geophys. Res.*, **73**:2069–2085 (1968)].

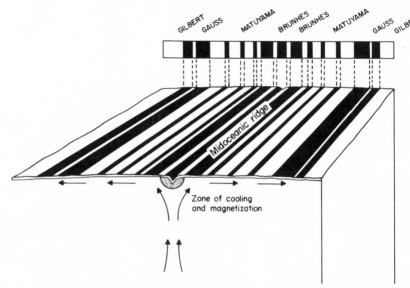

FIGURE 8-7 Schematic diagram showing the spreading ocean floor and the imprinting of the magnetic anomalies as the material cools through its Curie temperature [from Cox, Dalrymple, and Doell, Reversals of the Earth's Magnetic Field, *Sci. Am.*, **216**:44–54 (1967)].

in long linear features indicates some genetic relationship between the sea floor and the midocean ridge.

The dimensions and nature of the reversal patterns were interpreted in an interesting way by Larochelle and Morley of the Geological Survey of Canada and by Vine and Matthews of Cambridge, who noticed that there was a striking similarity between the reversal time scale already established on continental rocks and the highs and lows on the magnetic traces. Was it possible, they speculated, that the sea floor was originating at the midocean ridge and spreading laterally? The volcanic material, hot and molten, could come up along the midocean rift, known to be associated with high heat-flows values and extensive faulting, and then cool through the Curie temperature, acquiring a magnetization dictated by the magnetic field at that time. This material could then spread out laterally, carrying with it

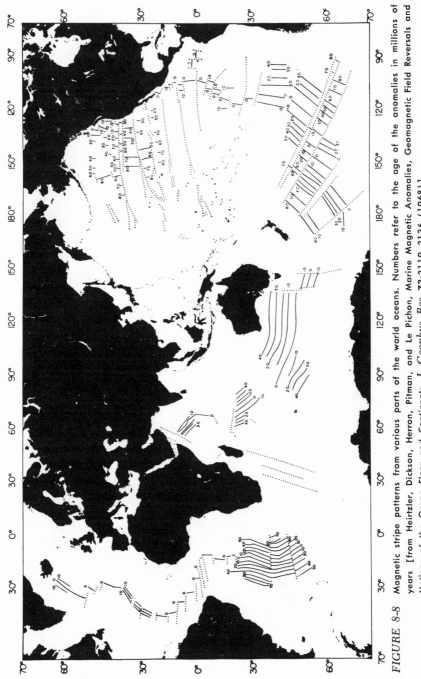

FIGURE 8-8 Magnetic stripe patterns from various parts of the world oceans. Numbers refer to the age of the anomalies in millions of years [from Heirtzler, Dickson, Herron, Pitman, and Le Pichon, Marine Magnetic Anomalies, Geomagnetic Field Reversals and Motions of the Ocean Floor and Continents, *J. Geophys. Res.* 73:2119–2136 (1968)].

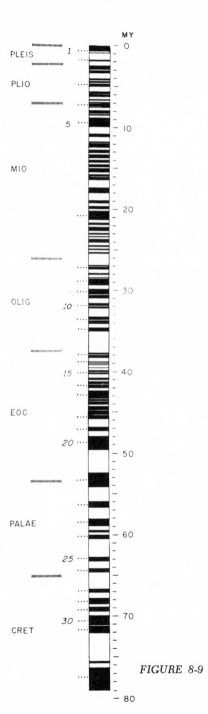

FIGURE 8-9 Reversal sequence to 80 million years based on sea-floor spreading patterns (same source as Fig. 8-8).

the pattern of the reversals. The essence of the idea is illustrated in Fig. 8-7. Thus, distance from the central midocean ridge would be a measure of time, an accurate measure if the spreading in fact took place at a constant rate.

Detailed comparison between the magnetic anomalies recorded on magnetometers and the record, now established for the past 6 million years, indicates that the rate of spreading for that time is about 1 to 5 cm/yr—much too slow to measure with present techniques but important enough to have profound geological and geophysical implications. The characteristic magnetic features found in the world's oceans are shown in Fig. 8-8.

Extension of the reversal time scale has been made back to 80 million years by extrapolation. The data do not show exactly uniform rates of spreading for all parts of the ocean floors but the values are surprisingly consistent. A first estimate is given in Fig. 8-9. Revision of this time scale may be needed as additional data from the continents become available, since beyond 6 my, the age is determined by reasonable extrapolation and could be modified to account for changing rates of spreading. The interesting point about these patterns is that there appears to have been no change in character in the reversal sequence over the last 80 million years. On the average, the field reverses about every 0.4 million years, and no characteristic preference is shown for either reversed or normal periods.

Until the actual movement of the sea floor can be directly detected, there will be some uncertainty in the model. However, the evidence for sea-floor spreading is mounting rapidly. It is almost impossible to imagine any other way of finding the major symmetry in magnetic anomalies around the ridges and the close correlation between known polarity events and the magnetic anomalies.

9

paleomagnetism: the dipole hypothesis, polar wandering, and continental drift

Since the subject of paleomagnetism is being pursued actively in many parts of the world, the nature of the magnetic field at various times in the past and in different parts of the world is being defined at a rapid rate. It is interesting to consider various aspects of the ancient field in order to assess its character. Perhaps the most important question to consider is whether it had a generally dipolar character in geologic time or whether it had some other more complex configuration. Looking at the present field as discussed in Chap. 4, we can readily see that at the present time it is not accurately dipolar, but only approximates this. Moreover, the dipole axis does not coincide precisely with the rotation pole unless a considerable amount of averaging over a period of time is done. It is, therefore, useful to test the dipolar hypothesis by looking at rocks of a single age and from a single continental block, where relative motions since the time of formation are unlikely. At the same time, if proper testing of the hypothesis is to be done, widely separated locations must be used. As a result, very few adequate tests are available.

Two sets of data will be considered here, but it is clear that many more tests ought to be carried out as more data become available. Rocks of Cretaceous age (65 to 136 my) in North America have received quite intensive studies. Sampling areas range from the Sierra Nevadas in the west, to southeastern Quebec in the east, and to the Arctic Islands in the north. Currently available data for North America are given in Appendix 4 (see Table 9-1 for geologic time table). These pole positions are plotted in Fig. 9-1. It is evident that the pole positions fall in a very small group just north of the Bering Sea and show very little scatter in spite of the considerable length of the Cretaceous period. Sampling, moreover, has covered almost a 90° variation in longitude, creating the impression that the field was indeed nearly dipolar in Cretaceous times. A nondipole field would lead to great dispersion. One odd group has a pole position in the middle Atlantic. The reason for this is unknown,

TABLE 9-1   **Geologic Time Table (after Holmes)**

Cenozoic	Quaternary	Recent	5000 yr
		Pleistocene	
	Tertiary	Pliocene	2.5 my
		Miocene	7 my
		Oligocene	26 my
		Eocene	38 my
		Paleocene	54 my
			65 my
Mesozoic	Cretaceous		136 my
	Jurassic		190 my
	Triassic		225 my
Paleozoic	Permian		280 my
	Pennsylvanian		325 my
	Mississippian		345 my
	Devonian		395 my
	Silurian		430 my
	Ordovician		500 my
	Cambrian		570 my
Precambrian			

FIGURE 9-1 Cretaceous pole positions for North America showing sample locations (X).

but it should be noted that the samples were collected from the Franciscan formation west of the San Andreas fault in California in a region of complex structure and recent movements. Perhaps the structures have changed position since they were last magnetized or perhaps an intermediate field direction was captured.

The second group of data examined in detail as a test of the dipole hypothesis is Triassic (190 to 225 my) data from North America and from the U.S.S.R., as shown in Fig. 9-2. Data from North America again consist of information from widely different parts of the continent. Data from the Canadian Atlantic provinces, from the Triassic valleys of the eastern United States, and from the Rocky Mountain region give quite a good grouping of pole positions. A few scattered points (Table A-4-1) are from early measurements that have never been fully tested

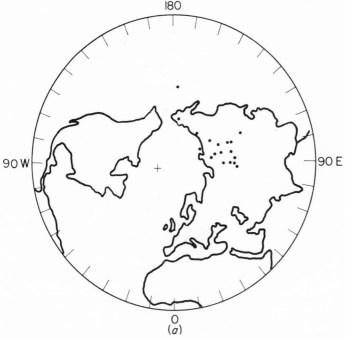

FIGURE 9-2 a Triassic pole positions from North America.
b Triassic pole positions from U.S.R.R. (from Khramov and Sholpo, Paleomagnetism, Nedra, Moscow, 1967):
circles = European U.S.S.R.
triangles = Siberian U.S.S.R.

for viscous effects and other processes. The second set of data from a recent compilation by Khramov and Sholpo in the U.S.S.R. also shows a good grouping with internal consistency for samples from the European and Siberian areas (from 21° longitude to 132° longitude). This is an extremely wide sampling within a single continent, and although there is some scatter in the data, there is no sign of a systematic variation across the continent, such as one might expect if the field were not dipolar.

It will be necessary to establish in as many cases as possible that the field had a roughly dipolar character for each interval of geologic time before one can have complete faith

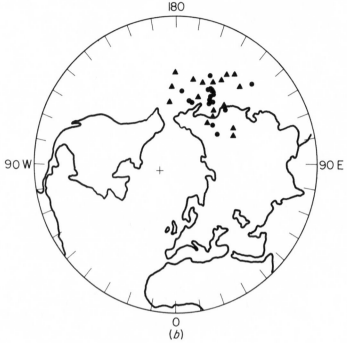

FIGURE 9-2 Continued.

in the general dipolar character of the field. However, where it has been tested in detail, the field appears to have this character, and it is therefore possible to begin making intercontinental correlation.

It is useful here to summarize very briefly the data available from each continent and then to make comparisons where appropriate.

NORTH AMERICA

The known paleomagnetic data from North America have been tabulated in Appendix 4 and are represented there in figures for the various geologic periods. Data are fairly adequate for upper and lower Tertiary, Cretaceous, Triassic, Permian, and Carboniferous times, but Jurassic-age rocks and lower Paleozoic rocks have been studied only in limited fashion.

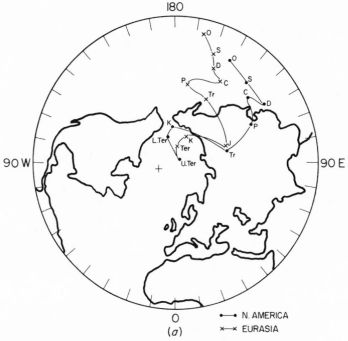

FIGURE 9-3   *a*   Pole positions for North America and Europe.
            b   Pole positions for Africa and South America.
            c   Pole positions for India and Australia.

(U. Ter = U. Tertiary; L. Ter = Lower Tertiary; K = Cretaceous; J = Jurassic; Tr = Triassic; P = Permian; C = Carboniferous; D = Devonian; O = Ordovician; S = Silurian;
€ = Cambrian. U, L, M refer to upper, lower, and middle.)
Circled points represent data in lower hemisphere.

European data: Krs, The Basic Elements of Paleomagnetic Geochronology, *Sbornik Geologicych Ved.* 5, 7–33
(1966). *South American data:* Creer, Paleomagnetic Data
from the Gondwanic Continents, in: A symposium on Continental Drift, Blackett, Bullard, and Runcorn (eds.) The
Royal Society of London, 1965. *African data:* McElhinny,
Briden, Jones, and Brock, Geological and Geophysical Implications of Paleomagnetic Results from Africa, *Rev. Geophysics,* 6: 201–238 (1968). *Indian data:* McElhinny,
Northward Drift of India—Examination of Recent Paleomagnetic Results, *Nature,* 217 (5126): 342–344 (1968).
Australian data: Briden, Recurrent Continental Drift of
Gondwanaland, *Nature,* 215, (5108): 1334–1339
(1967).

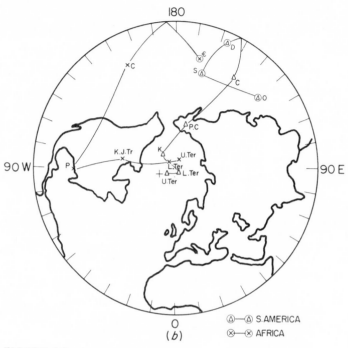

FIGURE 9-3 Continued.

and few data are available. Precambrian rocks have been studied to some extent between the ages of 600 my and 2500 my. The apparent pole relative to North America has distinctly followed a path from somewhere in the Pacific off the coast of Japan in late Paleozoic times to its present position (Fig. 9-3). There is, of course, no way of determining from this information alone whether this motion is due to the magnetic pole's moving or to the motion of the continent relative to the pole.

Independent tests are required to solve this important problem. If the magnetic pole has remained coupled to the rotation axis, then one can use geologic evidence about the nature of ancient climates. The assumption of a coupling between the two poles seems reasonable from our understanding of the origin of the field, as discussed previously, and it is a useful exercise to consider the nature of ancient climates and their relation

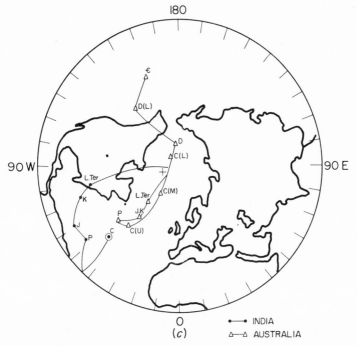

FIGURE 9-3   Continued.

to the rotation axis. No detailed studies will be given in this book, since this could be the topic of a whole new treatise. Rather, the reader is referred to the book by Irving (see References) and to books on paleoclimates which discuss the evidence in detail. The magnetic data for central North America indicate a latitude of 40 to 50° N for the period from Jurassic to the present, while during the Paleozoic and up until the Triassic, the central part of North America was close to the equator. Rocks formed in these older ages would then be expected to be characteristic of equatorial deposits if the general climatic conditions were similar to the present ones. This is indeed found to be the case by the distribution of extensive salt deposits, red sediments, and other rocks found in central North America, but much more detailed study will be required in order to put the conclusions of paleoclimatology on a sound basis.

EUROPE AND ASIA

A considerable amount of data is also available for Europe and the U.S.S.R. Data from the U.S.S.R. have been reviewed by Khramov and Sholpo and by Krs in 1966 (includes data from Europe). The data from Europe are not given here in detail, but the mean results compiled by Krs are shown in Fig. 9-3. Data from the Cretaceous and from the Jurassic are quite inadequate, and as in the case of North America, the data from the lower Paleozoic are quite incomplete. However, a distinct similarity is seen in the curves back to Cretaceous times. In Triassic times, the two poles appear to be separated by about 30°. A similar separation holds for Permian, Carboniferous, and Devonian times. The differences in the two curves could be the result of nondipolar components of the field in ancient times, but it is more likely that the differences are due to relative motions of the two continents. In this case, the magnetic data clearly indicate that the continents seem to have separated, that separation started during the Triassic or somewhat later, and that it was essentially completed sometime in the Cretaceous.

The separation of continents to form the Atlantic Ocean has been a topic of intense debate since the 1920s, when Wegener clearly outlined the evidence for continental drift. Many lines of argument both for and against continental drift have been given over the years, but the most convincing single piece of evidence is still the simple fit of continents that can be made by closing the Atlantic Ocean. The map in Fig. 9-4 shows the most recent attempts at reconstructing the continents by simply matching coastlines or at least the boundaries of the continental shelf approximated by the 500-fathom contour. The simple geometric fit is remarkable, involving only minor discrepancies, and these occur mainly in places of recent sedimentation. The geologic evidence on the African and South American coasts is quite clear. The deposition of sediments and volcanic activity in the lowest Cretaceous indicates that some rupturing and the formation of waterways between the two continents had already started by that time. One presumes, then, that the separation of the Atlantic continents began during Jurassic time.

This is in full agreement with the paleomagnetic data of Fig. 9-3a.

AFRICA

Rocks of various ages from Africa have been studied, and a preliminary polar wandering path has been determined by McElhinny et al., as shown in Fig. 9-3b. It can be seen that the polar path is quite different from the ones already discussed from North America and Europe. If the field sampled was indeed dipolar, the African data when compared with Eurasian and North American data make a good case for continental drift. After refitting the continents back together in the manner determined by Carey and by Bullard, the pole path coincides fairly well with that from North America during much of the Mesozoic period. The available data are limited, but the general trend is quite clear. The fit in pre-Cretaceous times with data from North America and Europe is not good, suggesting that continental movement has taken place. In pre-Carboniferous times, the data depart radically from those for North America and Europe, suggesting an earlier relative movement.

SOUTH AMERICA

Data available from South America have been summarized by Creer. The polar wandering pattern deduced from this is also shown in Fig. 9-3b, where it is seen that the general path is quite similar to that found for Europe and North America from the late Paleozoic to the present. The same curve refitted according to the continental positions shown in Fig. 9-4 shows again that during most of the Mesozoic period agreement with Europe, Africa, and North America is quite good.

It appears then that the continents were together during the period from Carboniferous to Triassic, and at this time the Atlantic opened and the continents moved to their present positions. It is not clear what position the continents were in before Carboniferous, but it is evident from the data that there may have been a period of drifting before the Carboniferous, which

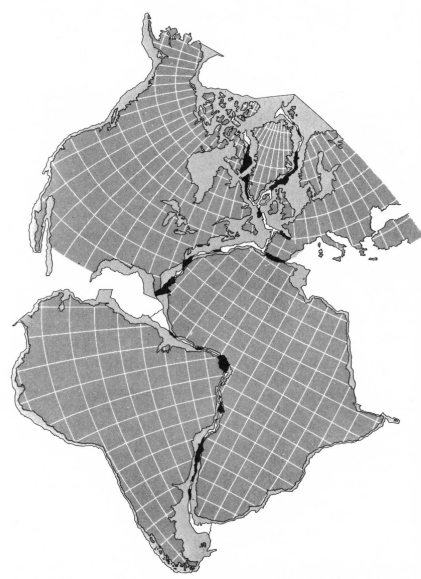

FIGURE 9-4   Reconstruction of the continents bordering the Atlantic at the 500-fathom depth line. Dark areas represent misfits (after Bullard, Everett, and Smith, The Fit of the Continents Around the Atlantic, in: A Symposium on Continental Drift, Blackett, Bullard, and Runcorn (eds.), Royal Society of London, 1965.)

brought these continents into juxtaposition. Then in Jurassic time the continents began to separate into their present positions, achieving this by about the middle or the end of the Cretaceous.

AUSTRALIA

A good deal of paleomagnetic work has also been done in Australia, and a fairly well-established polar wandering curve has been determined. This curve is shown in Fig. 9-3c. The pattern found here is entirely different from that found in the other continental blocks, in that the apparent pole has moved from a position in Carboniferous time, which is comparable to its present position, to the middle Atlantic position in Cretaceous and Jurassic times, and then back to its present position. This path is quite different in its general pattern from the other continents and indicates a probable movement of Australia with respect to the other continents.

INDIA

Data from India are appearing in increasing numbers and making an interesting study. The pole path so far determined is given in Fig. 9-3c. This path can be seen to be quite different from the other continental blocks, and it shows a large movement in the Tertiary. This movement, if it represents continental drift, means that India has moved from far south of the equator since the Deccan traps were formed about 50 million years ago. Previous to that time, little relative polar movement had taken place as far back as the Permian. The history of movement of India is proving to be most intriguing, in that it appears to have moved great distances in a short geologic time, and it seems to have undergone an entirely different history from Eurasia of which it is now a part. Evidently, independent motion of large blocks of present continents can take place as well as the motion of whole continents.

Some data are available from other parts of the world, but so far these are only a few isolated points, and no consistent pattern can be obtained to fit the overall picture. It is quite

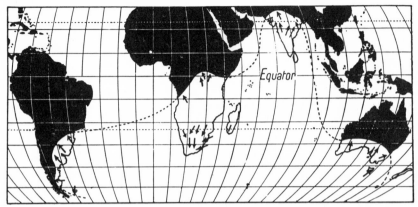

FIGURE 9-5   Distribution of Permo-Carboniferous glaciation in Gondwanaland. Arrows show direction of ice movement (from Holmes, Principles of Physical Geology, The Ronald Press Company, New York, 1965.)

useful to realize, however, that the data of paleomagnetism strongly support large continental movements, and in general the sense of motion is similar to that expected from Wegener's early ideas on continental drift. The fact that each continent seems to have an independent magnetic history and different drift rates at various geologic times strongly supports the idea that much of the apparent polar motion is in fact due to continental drift and not to polar wandering in a general sense.

OTHER OBSERVATIONS

Many other comparisons could be made, perhaps one of the most interesting being the evidence for glaciation. Geologists have long held that glaciation in the Permo-Carboniferous was quite extensive in the Southern Hemisphere. In the Quaternary, extensive glaciation took place in the Northern Hemisphere over the major land blocks, but most of the ice was limited to high latitudes, and only in a few places did it extend as far south as 40° of latitude. Assuming we can use the same rule for ancient glaciations, one would expect that the glaciations also took place at high latitudes. The figure shown as Fig. 9-5

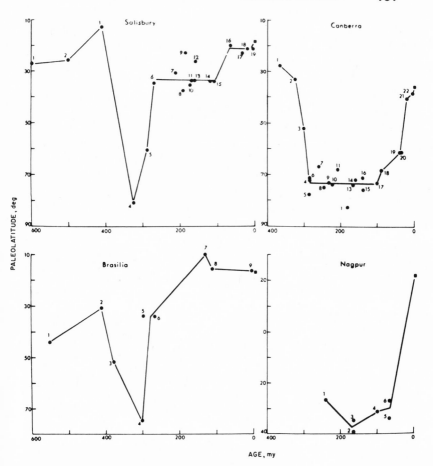

FIGURE 9-6   Paleolatitude variations for four cities in

    a   Africa.

    b   Australia.

    c   South America

    d   India.

    (Numbers from McElhinny, The Paleomagnetism of the Southern Continents, in press).

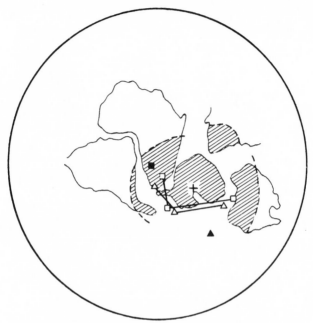

FIGURE 9-7   Permo-Carboniferous pole positions for southern continents when reassembled in position shown. Shaded areas represent glaciated areas. Note good agreement between rapid polar movement indicated for Africa and Australia.

☐   Africa
△   Australia
■   South America
▲   India

shows the distribution of glaciation known for the Permo-Carboniferous. This grouping of continents is often referred to as *Gondwanaland,* and it has long been thought that they represent parts of a single continental block. A useful check is to insure that the regions in question were indeed at high latitudes at the time in question. India and central Africa are in equatorial regions at present so that considerable movement is required to get these blocks into high latitudes. In Fig. 9-6 the paleolatitudes determined by paleomagnetic studies of these southern continents are given, and it is seen that indeed the areas of concern are all indicated to have been at high latitudes. India apparently reached only about 40° of latitude, but the others all reached to about 70 or 80°. It is possible, moreover, to reassemble the continental blocks in some manner to see if the Permo-Carboniferous poles are really coincident. Scanty data from Antarctica also support a high latitude for the Permo-Carboniferous. Although the agreement is not perfect, the poles shown in Fig. 9-3, when shifted to correspond to the distribution of land given in Fig. 9-7, show a much better grouping than when the continents are in their present position, supporting the idea that there was indeed a single continental block in which extensive glaciation took place.

Although many more data are clearly needed to back up the detailed pole-position curves from the various continents and continental blocks, many features are already clear. The earth's magnetic field appears to have been dipolar through much of history. The Atlantic Ocean appears to have been closed from Carboniferous to Jurassic times and then to have started opening, achieving the present distribution of Atlantic continents before the end of Cretaceous. The southern continents appear to have been grouped around the south pole during the extensive Permo-Carboniferous glaciation known from geologic evidence. This includes India, which appears to have migrated north to its present position only in Tertiary time. Undoubtedly, many more such features of the earth's history will be revealed as paleomagnetic data from the various crustal units become available. In particular, it is to be hoped that we will be able to get a clearer picture of the lower Paleozoic magnetic history.

One of the problems of solid-state physics which can be tackled quite simply is the estimation of the susceptibility of diamagnetic and paramagnetic materials.

Diamagnetism

Let us first consider the effect of interaction between orbiting charged particles and an applied magnetic field. If a field is applied to electrons as they spin around the nucleus, there is a tendency for the orbit to be modified in such a way as to shield the applied field. Each orbiting electron is under the influence of the Coulomb central force attracting it to the nucleus. This is proportional to e^2/r^2, where e is the charge on the electron, and r is the distance between the nucleus and the electron. The centrifugal force is $m w_0^2 r$, where m is the mass of the electron and w_0 the rotational frequency in the absence of an applied field:

$$m w_0^2 r = \frac{e^2}{r^2}$$

A moving charge has a force acting on it in the presence of a magnetic field given as $F = (e/c) \, wr \times H$, where w equals the rotational frequency, H the field, and c the speed of light.

The net effect of this force is to add an additional central force term so that

$$F = \frac{e^2}{r^2} - \frac{e}{c} wr \times H$$

This gives a value for w which is

$$w = \pm \left[\frac{(eH)^2}{2mc} + \frac{e^2}{mr^3} \right]^{1/2} - \frac{eH}{2mc}$$

$$\approx w_0 - \frac{eH}{2mc} \qquad \text{if } w_0 \gg \frac{eH}{2mc}$$

The result is that the external field modifies the orbit rotation speed by w_L or the Larmor frequency equals $-(eH)/2mc$.

The effect of changing the current slightly, then, is to modify the magnetic moment of the electron in orbit, since the spinning rate is slightly reduced. The equivalent current modification is given as

$$i = - \frac{Ze}{2\pi c} w_L$$

where i is the current, and Z is the atomic number or the number of electrons so affected. The magnetic moment μ which corresponds to this spinning current is given as $0.1\ iA$, where A is the cross-sectional area of the orbit.

The susceptibility Xa per atom is then given as

$$\frac{\mu}{H} = - \frac{Ze^2}{4mc^2} \overline{r^2}$$

where $\overline{r^2}$ is an average radius for all the particles involved.

Since the problem with real material is three dimensional, this form is modified slightly to correspond to the case for real solids. This gives

$$X = \frac{Ze^2}{6mc^2} \overline{r^2}N$$

as the susceptibility per unit volume, where N is the number of atoms per unit volume.

This expression is often referred to as the *Langevin diamagnetic expression*. The modification of the electronic orbit is thus seen to lead to a small negative change in the orbits under the influence of the applied field.

Paramagnetism

It is known that each individual electron behaves as if it had a permanent magnetization. This small magnet can respond to the presence of an applied field by rotating in the direction of the field. The magnetic energy of the electron spin is then at a minimum when the particles are aligned. However, the energies involved are very small, and thermal energy is always tending to disrupt the ordering with the result that the ordering of the spins by the magnetic field is a balance between the two processes. The magnetic energy V is $\mu H \cos \theta$, where θ is the angle between the field and the spin axis. The most common way to calculate the average value $\overline{(\cos \theta)}$ for $\cos \theta$ is to use Boltzmann statistics, which gives the probability of finding a spin with a certain orientation:

$$\overline{\cos\theta} = \frac{\int e^{-v/kt}\cos\theta\,d\Omega}{\int e^{-v/kt}\,d\Omega}$$

where $d\Omega$ is the element of solid angle, k is Boltzmann's constant, and T is the temperature in °K. This expression reduces to

$$L(a) = \overline{\cos\theta} = \coth a - \frac{1}{a}$$

where $a = \mu H/kt$. This expression is referred to as *Langevin's function* and can be used to calculate the paramagnetic susceptibility.

The magnetization per unit volume is

$$M = N\mu\left(\coth a - \frac{1}{a}\right)$$

If $\mu H/kt \ll 1$, so that the temperature is high or the field small as in most cases of interest, this reduces to

$$M = \frac{N\mu^2 H}{3kt}$$

The susceptibility is

$$X = \frac{M}{H} = \frac{N\mu^2}{3kt} = \frac{C}{T}$$

where C is a constant. This expression is called *Curie's law*, since he first recognized that the paramagnetic susceptibility was inversely proportional to temperature.

The phenomenon of ferromagnetism is due to interaction between atoms and could therefore be thought of as a study in cooperative processes. In the early days extensive studies of the simple magnetic interaction between particles were conducted. The magnetostatic interaction, even at typical interatomic distances, is quite negligible and cannot lead to ferromagnetism. It is now known that this phenomenon is due to another kind of interaction referred to as the *exchange interaction*. The precise reasons for it are difficult to explain without detailed quantum-mechanical discussions, but it is related to the fact that any given electron may be associated with more than one atom, thus providing a kind of electrical interaction. The result of this exchange is that the atoms tend to have a strong interaction which behaves as though a strong magnetic field were present in the material. Although fictitious, this field in reality gives a good phenomenological description of the ferromagnetic properties of materials. It is interesting to do a few calculations to get some idea of the properties of this field. Below some critical temperature the interaction dominates, but above this temperature, known as the *Curie temperature*, thermal disordering takes over and the behavior is that of a simple paramagnetic material. The thermal disordering energy at this temperature is kT_c, where k is Boltzmann's constant, and T_c is the Curie temperature. The magnetic ordering energy is given by μH_E, where μ is the magnetic moment, and H_E is the fictitious internal field. At the Curie temperature, these two energies are equal. All the quantities but H_E are known, and this gives $H_E \approx 10^6$ or 10^7 oe for typical ferromagnetic substances. It is possible from this field to determine the expected shape of the magnetization-vs.-temperature curve.

Figure A-2-1 depicts this. The first curve drawn (1) illustrates the law of paramagnetism in which $M = N\mu L(a)$, where $L(a)$ is defined in Appendix 1. This curve is used, since $L(a)$ is a function of $\mu H/kT$, and the field under consideration is the strong internal field. For complete saturation the spontaneous magnetization is not dependent on field or temperature. In the same figure, a plot of the spontaneous magnetization as a function of the internal field is given (2). This line is a straight line, since M_s is directly proportional to H_E (assumed),

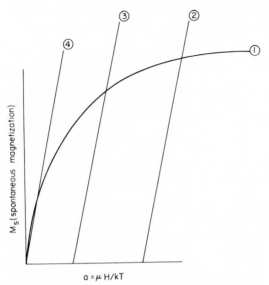

FIGURE A-2-1 Illustration of generation of spontaneous magnetization (see text for details).

that is,

$$M_s = \frac{H_E}{\lambda}$$

where λ is a constant, and M_s is the saturation magnetization. This means that $M_s = akT/\mu\lambda$. At low temperature, the curve relating M_s to a is given by the line (2), and as the temperature becomes higher, it progresses to (3) and to (4). The actual spontaneous magnetization is given by the intersection of line (1) with the other lines (2), (3), (4), . . . , as one moves to higher temperatures. Plotting the points generated in this way enables one to derive theoretical curves such as that found in Fig. 1-3.

APPENDIX 3 **PHYSICS OF FINE PARTICLES**

In the study of fine particles it is necessary to consider two cases. One is the region of transition in particle size from superparamagnetic to single domain, and the other is the transition from single domain to multidomain. Both of these cases are important in considering the highly stable magnetizations that are found in single-domain particles. The stability in such cases is controlled by the intrinsic properties of the material and not by the motion of domain walls. The approach adopted by Neel for the calculation of the superparamagnetic limit is given here. As particle sizes become smaller, thermal fluctuations can lead to a randomizing of the magnetic moments of individual grains. Neel accordingly adopted the concept of a relaxation time in order to develop the calculation.

This relaxation time τ_0 is given by

$$\frac{1}{\tau_0} = Ce^{-vE/2kT}$$

where C is a constant, v is the volume of the grain, E is a constant that depends on the energy barrier to be overcome, k is Boltzmann's constant, and T is absolute temperature. E can have a variety of different values and is a measure of the anisotropy that needs to be overcome in reversing the magnetization. This can arise from a variety of causes: shape anisotropy, magnetocrystalline anisotropy, or magnetostrictive anisotropy. In the case of uniaxial anisotropy there are only two easy directions of magnetization so that the following values can be assigned:

$$E \text{ shape} = (N_b - N_a)J_s^2$$

where N_b and N_a are the two demagnetizing factors, and J_s is the saturation magnetization.

$$E \text{ magnetocrystalline} = 2K_1'$$

where K_1' is the anisotropy coefficient.

$$E \text{ magnetostrictive} = 3\lambda_s\sigma$$

where λ_s is coefficient of magnetostriction, and σ is the internal stress.

It is possible, then, using the known properties of materials or the shape of particles, to estimate the critical volume of particles at which the material changes from superparamagnetic to single domain if the constant C is known. There are a variety of ways of estimating this value. Neel has shown that the elastic properties are important and that

$$C = \frac{eHc}{2m} \left(3G\lambda + DJ_s{}^2\right) \left(\frac{2v}{\pi GkT}\right)^{1/2}$$

where λ is the magnetostriction coefficient, G is the shear modulus, D is a numerical constant depending on grain shape, which is ≈ 3, and e and m are the charge and mass of the electron.

Using values appropriate for magnetite, it can be shown that the following values of v/T give the corresponding relaxation times:

v/T	τ_0 (sec)
5.52×10^{-21}	5.83×10^{-2}
11.05×10^{-21}	9.08
23.2×10^{-21}	3.04×10^{10}
27.6×10^{-21}	6.15×10^{13}
33.1×10^{-21}	1.56×10^{20}

Small changes in volume or temperature lead to very large differences in the relaxation time. This leads to the concept of a critical size or of a critical blocking temperature which acts much like a Curie temperature. The presence of a distribution of particle sizes in a given sample leads to a spectrum of blocking temperatures. Single-domain particles which are above the critical size and below the critical temperature are exceedingly stable magnetically. At room temperature, grains of magnetite larger than 0.01 or 0.02 μ will act as single-domain particles.

At the other end of the scale, as the particles become larger they eventually reach a size where it is energetically desirable to reduce the magnetostatic energy of the particle by introducing walls. The precise limit at which this takes place is difficult to estimate, since there are several variables involved, and people have generally resorted to using very simplified models for these estimates. These estimates are usually done by considering the shape, wall, and magnetocrystalline energies involved in any specific particle. One of the simplest cases to consider is that of an elongated particle, as done by Wohlfarth.

The magnetostatic energy or shape energy is given as $\frac{1}{2} N_a J_s{}^2$, where N_a is the demagnetizing factor in the direction of the magnetization. The magnetocrystalline energy will depend on the orientation of

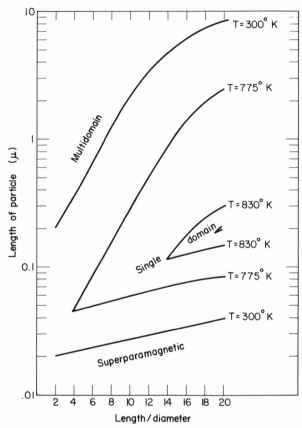

FIGURE A-3-1   Plot of transition from superparamagnetic
to single-domain behavior and from single-
domain to multidomain behavior for pro-
late ellipsoids of various sizes and shapes
at different temperatures [from Strangway,
Larson, and Goldstein, A Possible Cause
of High Magnetic Stability in Volcanic
Rocks, *J. Geophys. Res.,* **73**:3787–3795
(1968)].

the magnetization with respect to the magnetocrystalline axis and may take on any value ranging between K_1 and zero. The magnetostrictive effects may be important in cases of preferred stress directions but are ignored in this discussion. Wall energy values can be estimated quite readily, and several people have shown that a typical value is about 1 erg/cm². A particle then is single-domained as long as

$$\frac{\frac{1}{2}N_a J_s^2 + aK_1] \times \text{volume}}{1 \times \text{area}} < 1$$

where a is a constant between zero and 1, depending on the angle between the magnetocrystalline easy direction and the actual magnetization.

For particles with slight elongation, say, 2 or 3:1, the magnetostatic term is dominant and remains dominant until the elongation is on the order of 10:1. Many particles then are single-domained if

$$\frac{\frac{1}{2}N_a J_s^2 \times \text{volume}}{\text{area}} < 1$$

The set of curves given in Fig. A-3-1 illustrates this relationship for magnetite particles. The upper set of curves marks the limit between single-domain and multidomain particles of magnetite at the temperatures shown for the grain sizes and shapes. A wide range of particles can be single-domained. The lower curves in the same figure show the limit between superparamagnetic and single-domain behavior for the same particles. Similar calculations can be done for the other types of anisotropy, e.g., a spherical particle has only magnetocrystalline anisotropy. In general, particles greater than 0.1 to 1μ in size will be multidomain and less stable than the smaller particles.

It is interesting to estimate the coercive force of those particles which behave as single domains. For shape anisotropy the maximum effect is $2\pi Js$, for magnetocrystalline anisotropy it is $2K_1'/J_s$, and for magnetostrictive anisotropy it is $3\lambda_s\sigma/J_s$. This leads to corresponding values for the coercive force of magnetite of 2800, 600, and 750 oe. These are the maximum values possible, those only likely to be achieved for a few particles. The coercive force tends to be reduced by putting other grains nearby, i.e., grain interaction. In addition the process of reversing the magnetization may not be coherent. All of the individual spins may not reverse in the same way, and the actual coercive forces are likely to be considerably less than the above quoted values.

In this appendix a compilation of paleomagnetic data available for North America is presented. For the reader interested in details, reference should be made to the book by Irving (1964) and to articles in the *Geophysical Journal* by Irving and more recently by McElhinny. In these references complete listings for all continents and original references are given. Table A-4-1 shows only the pole position. In many cases radiometric-age dates are available; these are given after the sample name and location. For the Precambrian only radiometrically dated units are tabulated. Data from this table are plotted in Figs. A-4-1 to A-4-10.

TABLE A-4-1 Paleomagnetic Pole Positions for North America

Location and age	*Pole position*	
	(Lat)	*(Long)*
Quaternary:		
Pleistocene (0–2.58 my)		
New England glacial varves	79°N	128°E
Tertiary:		
Pliocene (2.5–7 my)		
Rio Grande lavas, N.Mex.		
(3.6–4.4 my)	85°N	109°E
Lousetown flows, Nev. (6.9 my)	16°N	156°W
Tertiary basalts of Yukon and		
British Columbia	85°N	150°E
Virgina City, Mont. (may be		
Miocene)	60°N	119°W
Miocene (7–26 my)		
Lovejoy basalt, Calif. (22–24 my)	No satisfactory mean	
Columbia plateau basalts, Ore.		
(14.5–21.3) my	86°N	26°E
Abert rim lava flows, Ore. (15 my)	76°N	74°E
Ellensburg fm, Wash. (10 my)	85°N	115°W
Oligocene (26–38 my)		
Gila mountains, SE Ariz. (28 my)	75°N	110°E

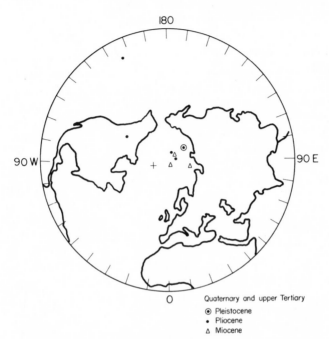

Quaternary and upper Tertiary
⊙ Pleistocene
• Pliocene
△ Miocene

FIGURE A-4-1 Quaternary and upper Tertiary data seem to group well around the present rotation pole. Exceptions are a set of flows from Nevada with an intermediate direction which likely represents a transistion direction, and an unusual direction reported from Virginia City, Montana.

TABLE A-4-1 Continued

Location and age	*Pole position*	
	(Lat)	*(Long)*
Volcanics, SW N.Mex. (29–33 my)	87°N	148°E
Gila Cliff Dwellings, N.Mex.	76°N	93°E
Eocene (38–54 my) and possibly *Paleocene* (54–65 my)		
Siletz River, Wash.	37°N	49°W
Green River, Colo.	78°N	158°W
Spanish Peaks, Colo.	81°N	149°W
Front Range Intrusive, Colo.	72°N	166°W
Beaverhead Valley, Mont.	66°N	121°W

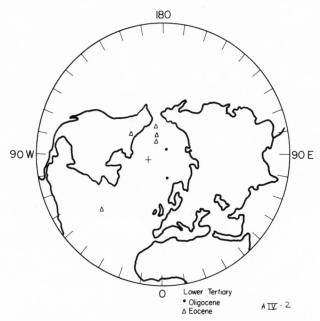

FIGURE A-4-2   Lower Tertiary data also group fairly well around the present rotation pole with a slight bias toward the Bering Strait area. This gives an indication of possible small relative movement between the magnetic pole and North America during Tertiary time. A single set of flows from the Siletz River area in Washington appears to have captured an intermediate direction of the field during a transition.

TABLE A-4-1 **Continued**

Location and age	Pole position	
	(Lat)	*(Long)*
Cretaceous (65–136 my)		
Monteregian Hills, Quebec		
(100–122 my)	70°N	171°E
Mt. Megantic, Quebec (115 my)	69°N	172°E
Granite Plutons, Sierra Nevada		
(83–90 my)	69°N	165°W
Isachsen Diabase, Northwest		
Territories (105 my)	69°N	180°E

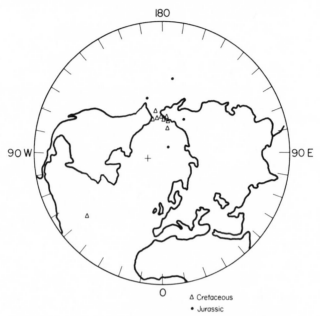

FIGURE A-4-3 Cretaceous data shown in this figure have a re-
markably consistent grouping and a mean pole
position in the Bering Straits is indicated. This is
quite clearly different from the present pole
position and represents definite relative motion
of pole and continent. The Franciscan formation
has an intermediate direction of magnetization
due either to tectonic movements or to the
capture of a transition zone. Only a few
Jurassic data are available, and these show
considerable scatter. The mean direction, however, is not greatly different from that of the
Cretaceous. Clearly more Jurassic data are required to establish the nature of the field in
this period.

TABLE A-4-1 **Continued**

Location and age	*Pole position*	
	(Lat)	*(Long)*
Boulder Batholith, Mont. (68–82 my)	76°N	167°E
Franciscan fm, Calif.	26°N	50°W

TABLE A-4-1 **Continued**

Location and age	Pole position	
	(Lat)	*(Long)*
Elkhorn Mtns, Mont.	69°N	171°W
Mesaverde fm, Wyo., Utah	70°N	177°E
Mt. Ascutney, Vt. (125–135 my)	64°N	173°W
Arkansas alkalic intrusives (98 my)	65°N	173°W
Jurassic (136–180 my)		
Guadelupe Mtns, Calif. (136 my)	43°N	171°E
Bucks pluton, Calif. (129–142 my)	58°N	165°W
White Mountains intrusives, N.H.		
(180 my)	85°N	126°E
Diabase dikes—Atlantic coast from		
Conn. to Ga. (may be Upper		
Triassic)	66°N	145°E
Triassic (190–225 my)		
Chugwater fm, Wyo.	48°N	112°E
Chinle fm, Ariz., Utah, Colo.,		
N.Mex.	55°N	93°E
New Oxford fm, Md.	66°N	174°E
Newark Group, N.J.	63°N	108°E
Connecticut Valley, Conn.	54°N	86°E
Diabase, Pa.	62°N	105°E
Nova Scotia diabase dike (197 my)	69°N	98°E
Lava, Mass.	55°N	88°E
Moenkopi, Ariz., Utah	57°N	107°E
Springdale, Ariz.	55°N	107°E
Upper Maroon, Colo.	56°N	100°E
Connecticut Valley, Deerfield, Mass.:		
volcanics (191 my)	66°N	105°E
associated redbeds	67°N	97°E
North Mountain basalt, Nova Scotia		
(200 my):		
(*a*)	73°N	104°E
(*b*)	66°N	113°E
Manicouagan, Quebec (225 my):		
(*a*)	57°N	89°E
(*b*)	61°N	89°E

FIGURE A-4-4   The available Triassic data provide a surprisingly good grouping with a mean pole
located in central Siberia. A single point
considerably away from the others is due to
early undemagnetized observations from the
New Oxford formation in Maryland. There is
little doubt that considerable motion took
place between continent and pole in the
interval of time from Triassic to Cretaceous.

TABLE A-4-1   Continued

Location and age	Pole position	
	(*Lat*)	(*Long*)
Permian (225–280 my)		
Cutler fm, Ariz., Colo.	34°N	107°E
Abo fm, N.Mex.	30°N	100°E
Yeso fm, N.Mex.	41°N	127°E
Supai fm, Ariz.	40°N	110°E
Sangre de Cristo fm, N.Mex.	38°N	81°E
Dunkard fm, W.Va.	44°N	122°E

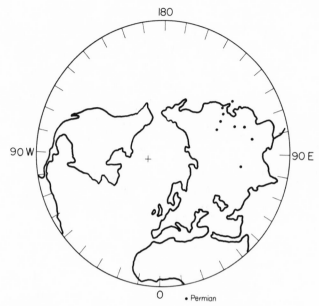

FIGURE A-4-5   Permian data are consistently reversed and
give a pole position in Mongolia on the main-
land of Asia. This pole is significantly different
from the Triassic one. The data are somewhat
scattered but since undemagnetized sets of
data are included the real scatter may be less.
In particular, the data for the Sangre de Cristo
formation in New Mexico need to be redone.

TABLE A-4-1   Continued

Location and age	Pole position	
	(Lat)	(Long)
Fountain and Lykins fm, Colo.	48°N	119°E
Maroon fm, Colo.	33°N	126°E
Basic sill, Prince Edward Island	52°N	113°E
Carboniferous (280–345 my)		
Barnett fm, Tex.	41°N	135°E
Naco fm, Ariz.	35°N	122°E
Hurley Creek fm, New Brunswick	39°N	125°E

FIGURE A-4-6   Carboniferous data are again fairly well grouped, giving a mean pole position on the Korean peninsula. This is distinctly different from the Premian pole position of Fig. A-4-5.

TABLE A-4-1   **Continued**

Location and age	Pole position	
	(Lat)	(Long)
Prince Edward Island redbeds:		
(a)	42°N	133°E
(b)	40°N	127°E
Pictou Group sst, New Brunswick	41°N	132°E
Bonaventure fm, New Brunswick	38°N	133°E
Codroy fm, Newfoundland	30°N	127°E
Upper Minturn fm, Colo.	39°N	105°E
Mauch Chunk, Pa.	51°N	132°E
Pre-Pictou sst, New Brunswick	24°N	133°E
Hopewell Group, New Brunswick	34°N	118°E

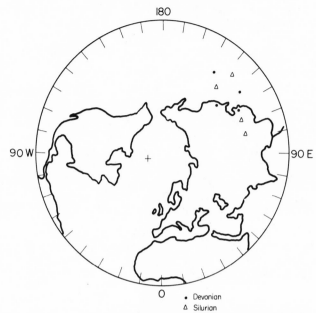

FIGURE A-4-7   Only scattered lower Paleozoic data are avail-
from North America, and it is difficult to do
more than indicate trends. The Devonian and
Silurian data in this figure give a mean pole
position in Japan, and no major difference
between this and the Carboniferous directions
can be observed. It appears therefore that the
period from Silurian to Carboniferous was one
of slow relative motion between the pole and
North America, while the period from Carboniferous to Cretaceous was one of rapid
relative motion.

TABLE A-4-1   **Continued**

Location and age	Pole position	
	(*Lat*)	(*Long*)
Devonian (345–395 my)		
Perry fm, New Brunswick	32°N	118°E
Perry fm, Me.	24°N	127°E
Catskill fm, Pa.	43°N	130°E
Clam Bank Group, Newfoundland	28°N	146°E

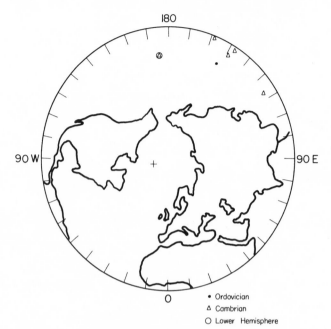

FIGURE A-4-8   Ordovician and Cambrian data are significantly
different from other Paleozoic data, indicating
another period of rapid polar motion. A few
scattered data points west of the Marshall
Islands in the Pacific indicate the general pole
position for the oldest Paleozoic. The Lodore
formation gives an unusual position which
ought to be redone. This effect may be due to
inadequate cleaning, or it may be due to a
transition involved in this sample group.

TABLE A-4-1   **Continued**

Location and age	Pole position	
	(Lat)	(Long)
Silurian (395–430 my)		
Rosehill fm, Md.	20°N	136°E
Clinton Iron Ore, Ala.	34°N	139°E
Bloomsburg fm, Pa:		
(a)	32°N	102°E
(b)	31°N	112°E

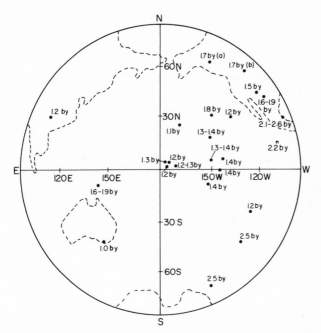

FIGURE A-4-9   In this figure, data from dated Precambrian units are presented. It is evident that there is a large scatter. This is in part due to the wide range of ages involved. All the dated units involved are over 10⁹ years in age. A well-defined pattern is not observed, but most of the pole positions are in the Pacific area. A specific grouping of units dated at 1.1–1.3 by is noted in the very center of the figure. Older units of about 1.3–1.4 by appear to cluster near the equator at about 150°W, and units of 1.5–1.6 by group near Baja California. These patterns are only very general, and much more work is needed to elucidate the Precambrian magnetic history in detail.

TABLE A-4-1   **Continued**

Location and age	*Pole position*	
	(Lat)	*(Long)*
Ordovician (430–500 my)		
Juniata fm, Pa.	20°N	153°E
Cambrian (500–570 my)		
Ratcliffe-Brook fm, New Brunswick	10°N	124°E

TABLE A-4-1 **Continued**

Location and age	Pole position	
	(*Lat*)	(*Long*)
Bradore fm, Newfoundland	9°N	149°E
Wichita Granites, Okla. (525 my)	2°N	147°E
Wilberns fm, Tex.	0	158°E
Lodore fm, Utah	23°N	6°E
Precambrian (dated units only)		
Front Range granites, Colo. (1.4 by)	8°S	151°W
Sierra Ancha diabase, Ariz. (1.1 by)	25°N	168°W
Sudbury dike swarm, Ontario		
(1.2–1.3 by)	2°N	171°W
Allard Lake anorthosite, Quebec		
(1.0 by)	39°S	140°E
Cobalt group sediments, Ontario		
(2.1–2.6 by)	22°N	97°W
Nipissing diabase sill, Ontario		
(2.2 by)	12°N	106°W
Negaunee iron ore, magnetite bands,		
Ontario (1.6–1.9 by)	33°N	105°W
Negaunee iron ore, hard hematite,		
Ontario (1.6–1.9 by)	8°S	144°E
Abitibi dike swarm, Quebec (1.2 by):		
(*a*) ENE(W)	27°N	134°W
(*b*) ENE(N)	24°N	107°E
(*c*) NNE	21°S	122°W
Matachewan dikes, Ontario (2.5 by):		
(*a*)	37°S	121°W
(*b*)	63°S	119°W
Marathon dikes, Ontario (1.8 by)	29°N	147°W
Molson dikes, Manitoba (1.5 by)	36°N	109°W
Mackenzie dikes, Northwest		
Territory (1.3 by)	4°N	177°W
Muskox gabbro, Northwest		
Territory (1.2 by)	4°N	175°W
Coppermine lavas, Northwest		
Territory (1.2 by)	1°N	176°W
Volcanics, SE Mo. (1.3–1.4 by)	5°N	150°W

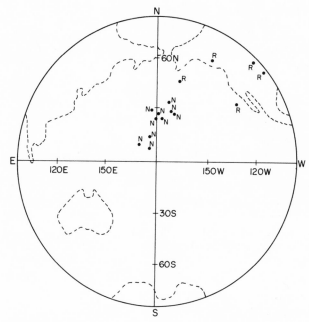

FIGURE A-4-10   A large amount of data from Keweenawan rocks of the Lake Superior area have been studied in some detail and are plotted separately in this figure. It is of particular interest to note that the normal units fall in a distinct group separate from the reversed units. One possible explanation is that the normal units are of a different age from the reversed ones, and some polar movement took place in the meantime. A second possibility is that there has been some remagnetization since the original and a vector component has been added. If this was added in equal amounts to both normal and reversed rocks, the mean apparent pole positions for these rocks is close to that found in Fig. A-4-9 for rocks in the same age range. Further elucidation awaits data from units of the same age in other areas.

TABLE A-4-1   Continued

Location and age	Pole position	
	(Lat)	(Long)
Sudbury basin, Ontario (1.7 by):		
(a) (no correction)	58°N	130°W
(b) (structural correction made)	47°N	107°W

TABLE A-4-1 **Continued**

Arbuckle granites, Okla. (1.3–1.4 by)	17°N	150°W
Croker Island Complex, Ontario		
(1.5 by)	5°N	143°W
Michikamau anorthosite, Labrador		
(1.4 by)	0.5°S	145°W
Precambrian (Keeweenawan, 0.9–1.2 by)		
Logan sills (R)	54°N	130°W
North Shore volcanics (R)		
(Grand Portage)	45°N	163°W
Baraga Co. dikes (R)	45°N	96°W
South Range—Ironwood lavas (R)	29°N	128°W
Alona Bay lavas (R)	39°N	95°W
Portage lake lavas (N):		
(*a*)	27°N	169°W
(*b*)	24°N	177°W
(*c*)	27°N	179°W
Copper Harbor lavas and		
sediments (N):		
(*a*)	13°N	176°E
(*b*)	29°N	177°E
Logan diabase (N)	33°N	172°W
Duluth gabbro (N)	24°N	180°E
Beaver Bay complex (N)	28°N	171°W
Freda and Nonesuch:		
(*a*)	9°N	170°E
(*b*)	7°N	176°E

SELECTED REFERENCES

chapter 1

Bates, L. F.: "Modern Magnetism," Cambridge University Press, New York, 1951.

Brown, W. F.: "Magnetostatic Principles in Ferromagnetism," North-Holland Publishing Co., Amsterdam, 1962.

Chikazumi, S.: "Physics of Magnetism," John Wiley & Sons, Inc., New York, 1964.

Irving, E.: "Paleomagnetism and Its Application to Geological and Geophysical Problems," John Wiley & Sons, Inc., New York, 1964.

Morrish, A. H.: "The Physical Principles of Magnetism," John Wiley & Sons, Inc., New York, 1965.

Nagata, T.: "Rock Magnetism," 2d ed., Maruzen Press, Ltd., 1961.

Neel, L.: Some Theoretical Aspects of Rock Magnetism, *Adv. Phys.*, **4**:191–243 (1955).

Smit, J., and H. P. J. Wijn: "Ferrites," John Wiley & Sons, Inc., New York, 1959.

Stacey, F. D.: The Physical Theory of Rock Magnetism, *Adv. Phys.*, **12**:45–133 (1963).

chapter 2

Deer, W. A., R. A. Howie, and J. Zussman: "Rock-Forming Minerals," vol. 5, "Non-Silicates," John Wiley & Sons, Inc., New York, 1962.

Mee, C. D.: "The Physics of Magnetic Recording," North-Holland Publishing Co., Amsterdam, 1964.

Mulay, L. N.: 1963, "Magnetic Susceptibility," pp. 1751–1853, Interscience Publishers, New York, 1963.

Nagata, T., and M. Ozima: Paleomagnetism, in "Physics of Geomagnetic Phenomena," S. Matsushita and W. H. Campbell (eds.), Academic Press, Inc., New York, 1967.

Nicholls, G. D.: The Mineralogy of Rock Magnetism, *Adv. Phys.*, **4**:113–190 (1955).

chapter 3

Blackett, P. M. S.: "Lectures on Rock Magnetism," Weizmann Science Press, 1956.

Dunlop, D., and G. F. West: An Experimental Evaluation of Single Domain Theories, *Rev. Geophys.* **7**:709–759 (1969).

Larson, E. E., M. Ozima, M. Ozima, T. Nagata, and D. W. Strangway: Stability of the Remanent Magnetization of Rocks, *Geophys. J.,* **17**:263–292 (1969).

chapter 4

Chapman, S., and J. Bartels: "Geomagnetism," Clarendon Press, Oxford, 1940.

Jacobs, J. A.: "The Earth's Core and Geomagnetism," The Macmillan Company, New York, 1963.

Hide, R.: The Hydrodynamics of the Earth's Core, in "Physics and Chemistry of the Earth," vol. 1, Pergamon Press, New York, 1956.

Hide, R., and P. H. Roberts: The Origin of the Main Geomagnetic Field, in "Physics and Chemistry of the Earth," vol. 4, Pergamon Press, New York, 1961.

Hindmarsh, W. R., F. J. Lowes, P. H. Roberts, and S. K. Runcorn (eds.): "Magnetism and the Cosmos," American Elsevier Publishing Company, Inc., New York, 1967.

Matsushita, S., and W. H. Campbell. "Physics of Geomagnetic Phenomena," Academic Press, Inc., New York, 1967.

Nagata, T.: "Benedum Earth Magnetism Symposium," University of Pittsburgh Press, Pittsburgh, 1962.

Rikitake, T.: "Electromagnetism and the Earth's Interior," American Elsevier Publishing Company, Inc., New York, 1966.

chapter 5

Chamalaun, F. H., and K. M. Creer. Thermal Demagnetization Studies of the Old Red Sandstone of the Anglo-Welsh Cuvette, *J. Geophys. Res.,* **69**:1607–1616 (1964).

Collinson, D. W., and K. M. Creer: Measurements in Paleomagnetism, in "Methods and Techniques in Geophysics," Interscience Publishers, Inc., New York, 1960.

Collinson, D. W., K. M. Creer, and S. K. Runcorn: "Methods in Paleomagnetism," American Elsevier Publishing Company, Inc., New York, 1967.

Doell, R. R., and A. Cox: Paleomagnetism, in "Advances in Geophysics," vol. 8, Academic Press, Inc., New York, 1961.

Fisher R. A.: Dispersion on a Sphere, *Proc. Roy. Soc. (London)*, **(A)217**:295–305 (1953).

Graham, J. W.: The Stability and Significance of Magnetism in Sedimentary Rocks, *J. Geophys. Res.*, **54**:131–167 (1949).

Wilson, R. L.: The Paleomagnetism of Baked Contact Rocks and Reversals of the Earth's Magnetic Field, *Geophys. J.*, **7**: 194–202 (1962).

chapter 6

Coe, R., The Determination of Paleointensities of the Earth's Magnetic Field with Emphasis on Mechanisms Which Could Cause Non-ideal Behaviour in Thellier's Method. *J. Geomag. Geoelec.*, **19**:157–179 (1967).

Coe, R., Paleointensities of the Earth's Magnetic Field Determined from Tertiary and Quaternary Rocks, *J. Geophys. Res.*, **72**: 3247–3262 (1967).

Koenigsberger, J. G.: Natural Residual Magnetism of Eruptive Rocks, pt 1 and 2, *Terr. Magn. Atmos. Elec.*, **43**:119 (1938).

Smith, P. J.: The Intensity of the Ancient Geomagnetic, a Review and Analysis, *Geophys. J.*, **12**:321–362 (1967).

Thellier, E., and O. Thellier: Sur l'intensité du Champ Magnétique Terrestre dans le Passé Historique et Géologique, *Ann. Geophys.*, **15**:285–376 (1959).

chapter 7

Burlatskaya, S. P., Archeomagnetic Evidence of the Earth's Magnetic Field Near Tiflis during the Past, *Am. Geophys. Union*, **1**:707 (1961).

DuBois, R. L., and N. Watanabe: Preliminary Results of Investigations Made to Study the Use of Indian Pottery to Determine the Paleointensity of the Geomagnetic Field for the United States A.D. 600–1400, *J. Geomag. Geoelec.*, **17**:417 (1965).

Kawai, N., and K. Hirooka: Wobbling Motion of the Geomagnetic Dipole Field in Historic Time during These 2000 Years. *J. Geomag. Geoelec.*, **19**:217–227 (1967).

Watanabe, N.: The Direction of Remanent Magnetism of Baked Earth and its Application to Chronology for Anthropology and Archaeology in Japan, *J. Fac. Sci. Univ. Tokyo*, **2**:1 (1959).

Weaver, K. F.: Magnetic Clues Help Date the Past, *Nat. Geograph.*, **131**:696–701 (1967).

chapter 8

Cox, A., R. R. Doell, and G. B. Dalrymple: Time Scale for Geomagnetic Reversals, in "History of the Earth's Crust," Princeton University Press, Princeton, N.J. (1968).

Heirtzler, J. R., G. O. Dickson, E. M. Herron, W. C. Pitman III, and X. Le Pichon: Marine Magnetic Anomalies, Geomagnetic Field Reversals and Motions of the Ocean Floor and Continents. *J. Geophys. Res.*, **73**:2119–2136 (1968).

McDougall, I., and F. H. Chamalaun: Geomagnetic Polarity Scale of Time, *Nature*, **212**:1415 (1968).

Momose, K.: Studies on the Variation of the Earth's Magnetic Field during Pliocene Times, *Bull. Earthquake Res. Inst.*, **41**:487 (1963).

Neel, L.: L'inversion de l'Aimantation Permanente des Roches, *Ann. Geophys.*, **7**:90–102 (1951).

Ninkovich, D., N. Opdyke, B. C. Heezen, and J. H. Foster: Paleomagnetic Stratigraphy, Rates of Deposition and Tephrachronology in North Pacific Deep-sea Sediments, *Earth Planet. Sci. Letts.*, **1**:476 (1966).

Uyeda, S.: Thermoremanent Magnetism as a Medium of Paleomagnetism, with Special Reference to Reverse Thermoremanent Magnetism, *Japan J. Geophys.*, **2**:1–123 (1958).

Van Ziji, J. S. V., K. W. T. Graham, and A. L. Hales: The Paleomagnetism of the Stormberg Lavas II. The Behavior of the Magnetic Field during a Reversal, *Geophys. J.*, **7**:169 (1962).

Vine, F. J., and D. H. Matthews: Magnetic Anomalies Over Oceanic Ridges, *Nature*, **199**:(4897). 947–949 (1963).

chapter 9

Blackett, P. M. S., Sir E. Bullard, and S. K. Runcorn: "A Symposium on Continental Drift," The Royal Society, 1965.

Briden, J. C.: Recurrent Continental Drift of Gondwanaland, *Nature*, **215**:(5108) 1334–1339 (1967).

Creer, K. M.: A Synthesis of World-wide Paleomagnetic Data, in

"Mantles of the Earth and Terrestrial Planets," Interscience Publishers, Inc., New York, 1967.

Eicher, D. L.: "Geologic Time," Prentice-Hall, Inc., Englewood, N.J., 1968.

Holmes, A.: "Principles of Physical Geology," The Ronald Press Company, New York, 1965.

Khramov, A. H., and L. E. Sholpo: "Paleomagnetism," Nedra, Moscow, 1967.

Krs, M.: The Basic Elements of Paleomagnetic Geochronology, *Svonik Geolog., ved.,* **5**:7–33 (1966).

McElhinny, M. W., J. C. Briden, D. L. Jones, and A. Brock; Geological and Geophysical Implications of Paleomagnetic Results from Africa, *Rev. Geophys.,* **6**:201–238 (1968).

Nairn, A. E. M.: "Descriptive Paleoclimatology," Academic Press, Inc., New York, 1961.

Runcorn, S. K.: "Continental Drift," Academic Press, Inc., New York, 1961.

Wegener, A.: "The Origin of Continents and Oceans," Dover Publications, Inc., New York, 1966.

index

history of the earth's magnetic field

THE EARTH AND PLANETARY
SCIENCE SERIES

This is an introduction to the field
of rock magnetism and paleomagnetism, covering those topics
which have contributed to the
concepts of continental drift and
sea-floor spreading.

The first part of the book is an
introduction to the physics of
magnetism in geologic materials.
This is followed by a review of the
procedures adopted by those
attempting to reconstruct the history of the earth's field. Later
chapters are on the recent or
archaeologic history and on the
older or geologic history of the
magnetic field. The final chapters
cover applications to global
problems.

Features include elementary
yet exhaustive treatment of a field
characterized by constant advancement, simplified coverage of
the concepts of rock magnetism,
review of the evidence supporting
field reversals and discussion of
sea-floor spreading, and coverage
of the modern magnetic evidence
supporting continental drift.

The approach is descriptive,
but more quantitative discussions
are found in the appendices.